D0982839

SELECTED WRITINGS OF
JULES SUPERVIELLE

JULES SUPERVIELLE

SELECTED WRITINGS

NEW DIRECTIONS

The French text of the poems in this book follows that of the several volumes of Supervielle's works published by Librairie Gallimard, Paris.
The Alan Pryce-Jones translation of *Le Voleur d'enfants* was published in England in 1950 under the title *The Colonel's Children* by Martin Secker and Warburg Ltd. in association with Sidgwick and Jackson Ltd.

Library of Congress catalog card number: 66-11415

New Directions Books are published for James Laughlin by
New Directions Publishing Corporation,
333 Sixth Avenue, New York 10014.

CONTENTS

POEMS (bilingual section)

v

STORIES

NOVEL

POETRY

translated by James Kirkup, Denise Levertov, and Kenneth Rexroth

DERRIERE CE CIEL ETEINT . . .

Derrière ce ciel éteint et cette mer grise
Où l'étrave du navire creuse un modeste sillon,
Par delà cet horizon fermé,
Il y a le Brésil avec toutes ses palmes,
D'énormes bananiers mêlant leurs feuilles comme des élé-
    phants leurs mouvantes trompes,
Des fusées de bambous qui se disputent le ciel,
De la douceur en profondeur, un fourré de douceur,
Et de purs ovales féminins qui ont la mémoire de la volupté.
Voici que peu à peu l'horizon s'est décousu,
Et la terre s'est allongé une place fine.
Apparaissent des cimes encore mal sorties du néant, mais qui
    tout de suite malgré les réticences des lointains,
Ont le prestige des montagnes.
Déjà luisent des maisons le long de la bruissante déchirure
    des plages;
Dans le glissement du paysage, sur un plan huilé,
Déjà voici une femme assise au milieu d'un suave champ de
    cannes,
Et parvient jusqu'à moi
La gratitude de l'humus rouge après les tropicales pluies.

A UNE ENFANT

Que ta voix à travers les portes et les murs
Me trouve enfin dans ma chambre, caché par la poésie,
O enfant qui es mon enfant,

BEHIND THIS DEADENED SKY

Behind this deadened sky, this grey sea
in which the ship's prow scoops a middling furrow,
beyond that closed horizon
there lies Brazil with all its palms,
giant banana trees, like elephants with weaving trunks,
that tangle leaf with leaf,
bamboo rockets, all jostling for an inch of sky,
a profundity of ease, a jungle laxness,
and the girls' pure oval faces, memory of sensual delight.
Here the horizon's seam is gradually split,
and earth slips in a narrow tongue of land.
Peaks still half-lost in nothingness appear,
and yet, despite the reserve of distant things,
proclaim themselves as mountains.
Houses already are glimmering along the thunderous gash of
      the beaches;
here in the landscape that slips away with an oily smoothness
there is a woman sitting alone in a balmy field of sugar cane,
and there is the trace
of the red earth's gratitude, after the tropic rains.

[J.K.]

TO A LITTLE GIRL

O, let your voice, sounding the doors and the walls,
Find me at last in my room, in a maze of poetry, child,
You who are my child,

Toi qui as l'étonnement de la corbeille peu à peu garnie de
fleurs et d'herbes odorantes
Quand elle se croyait oubliée dans un coin,
Et tu regardes de mon côté comme en pleine forêt l'écriteau
qui montre les routes.
La peinture est visible à peine,
On confond les distances
Mais on est rassuré.

O dénuement!
Tu n'es même pas sûre de posséder ta petite robe ni tes pieds
nus dans tes sandales
Ni que tes yeux soient bien à toi, ni même leur étonnement,
Ni cette bouche charnue, ni ces paroles retenues,
As-tu seulement le droit de regarder du haut en bas ces arbres
qui barrent le ciel du jardin
Avec toutes ces pommes de pin et ces aiguilles qui fourmillent?
Le ciel est si large qu'il n'est peut-être pas de place en dessous
pour une enfant de ton âge,
Trop d'espace nous étouffe autant que s'il n'y en avait pas
assez.
Et pourtant il te faut, comme les personnes grandes,
Endurer tout l'univers avec son sourd mouvement;
Même les fourmis s'en accommodent et les petits des fourmis.
Comment faire pour accueillir les attelages sur les routes, à des
vitesses différentes,
Et les chaudières des navires qui portent le feu sur la mer?
Tes yeux trouveraient dans les miens le secours que l'on peut
tirer
De cette chose haute à la voix grave qu'on appelle un père
dans les maisons
S'il ne suffisit de porter un regard clair sur le monde.

You who wear the astonished look of a jug that is filled with
     flowers and sweet-smelling grasses,
Though it thought it would always lie there forgotten in
     the corner;
And you face me like a signpost at the heart of a forest,
     pointing the way.
One can hardly make out what it says,
And one place seems as far away as the other,
But it gives one a sense of security.

O, forsaken one!
You cannot even be sure you possess your own little frock or
     your bare feet in your sandals,
Or be sure that your eyes are really your own, or express their
     own astonishment even,
Or be sure of that plump little mouth with its cautious words.
Have you even the right to look at these trees that prison
     the garden sky
With all their pine cones and their teeming needles?
The sky is so vast—perhaps there is no proper place beneath it
     for such a little child as you!
We are stifled by too much space, just as we are by too little;
And yet, just like a grown-up person, you must learn to bear
The entire universe and all its moving heaviness;
Even the ants get used to it, and their little ones too.
What will you do about the traffic on the roads, with its
     varying speeds,
And the stokeholes of liners that carry their flames out
     over the water?
—Your eyes would discover in my own
All the protection you desire from
That tall being with the deep voice that is called a father
     in the houses,
If casting a clear gaze upon the world were not enough for you.

                                   [J.K.]

APPARITION

A Max Jacob

Où sont-ils les points cardinaux,
Le soleil se levant à l'Est,
Mon sang et son itinéraire
Prémédité dans mes artères?
Le voilà qui déborde et creuse,
Grossi de neiges et de cris
Il court dans des régions confuses;
Ma tête qui jusqu'ici
Balançait les pensées comme branches des îles,
Forge des ténèbres crochues.
Ma chaise que happe l'abîme
Est-ce celle du condamné
Qui s'enfonce dans la mort avec toute l'Amérique?

Qui est là? Quel est cet homme qui s'assied à notre table
Avec cet air de sortir comme un trois-mâts du brouillard,
Ce front qui balance un feu, ces mains d'écume marine,
Et couverts les vêtements par un morceau de ciel noir?
A sa parole une étoile accroche sa toile araigneuse,
Quand il respire il déforme et forme une nébuleuse.
Il porte, comme la nuit, des lunettes cerclées d'or
Et des lèvres embrasées où s'alarment des abeilles,
Mais ses yeux, sa voix, son cœur sont d'un enfant à l'aurore.
Quel est cet homme dont l'âme fait des signes solennels?
Voici Pilar, elle m'apaise, ses yeux déplacent le mystère.
Elle a toujours derrière elle comme un souvenir de famille

APPARITION

Where have they gone, the points of the compass?
Where are the cardinal points,
The sun that rises in the East,
My blood that maps its customary
Route along my arteries?
Now it is overflowing and plunging,
Swollen with snows and cries,
Running over uncharted regions.
My head that until now
Was weighing its thoughts like island branches
Is hammering out a spiky shade.
Can my chair that a canyon snatches
Be the one the condemned man sits in
As he plunges deep into death with the whole of America?

Who is there? Who is that man who sits at our table
As if he were coming up out of the fog like a tall three-master,
High on his head a lantern swinging,
His hands made of ocean foam,
And his clothes hidden
Under an odd fragment of black sky?
On a word from him, a star spins its spidery light,
When he breathes it takes on the form and the formlessness of
    a nebula.
Like the night, he wears spectacles framed in gold
He has blazing lips that startle the bees,
But his eyes, his voice, his heart are those of a child at the
    break of day.
Who is this man whose soul is solemnly beckoning?
Here is Pilar, she calms my fears, her eyes defy the mystery.
Always behind her there is the memory of home and family,

Le soleil de l'Uruguay qui secrètement pour nous brille,
Mes enfants et mes amis, leur tendresse est circulaire
Autour de la table ronde, fière comme l'univers;
Leurs fraise sourires s'en vont de bouche en bouche fidèles,
Prisonniers les uns des autres, ce sont couleurs d'arc-en-ciel.

Et comme dans la peinture de Rousseau le douanier,
Notre tablée monte au ciel voguant dans une nuée.

Nous chuchotons seulement tant on est près des étoiles,
Sans cartes ni gouvernail, et le ciel pour bastingage.

Comment vinrent jusqu'ici ces goélands par centaines
Quand déjà nous respirons un angélique oxygène.

Nous cueillons et recueillons du céleste romarin,
De la fougère affranchie qui se passe de racines,
Et comme il nous est poussé dans l'air pur des ailes longues
Nous mêlons notre plumage à la courbure des mondes.

LE SURVIVANT

A Alfonso Reyes

Lorsque le noyé se réveille au fond des mers et que son cœur
Se met à battre comme le feuillage du tremble,
Il voit approcher de lui un cavalier qui marche l'amble
Et qui respire à l'aise et lui fait signe de ne pas avoir peur.

Il lui frôle le visage d'une touffe de fleurs jaunes

The sun of Uruguay that shines for us in secret,
My children and my friends, their kindness encircling
The circular table that is as proud as the universe;
Their fresh smiles go from mouth to faithful mouth,
They are each other's prisoners, like the colors of the rainbow.

And as in the picture by the Douanier Rousseau,
Our table ascends to the heavens, borne on a cloud.

We are only whispering, we are so close to the stars,
Without maps, and rudderless, with only the sky for bulwarks.

How did they get here, these hundreds of seagulls,
When we're already breathing the air the angels breathe?

We pluck, and pluck again, celestial rosemary,
And sublime ferns that do without roots,
And as we have sprouted long wings in the air,
We mingle our plumage with the curving worlds.

                                                    [J.K.]

THE SURVIVOR

                              For Alfonso Reyes

When the drowned man awakens at the bottom of the ocean
      and his heart
Begins to flutter like an aspen leaf
He sees riding gently towards him a horseman
Who breathes without difficulty and motions to him not to
      be afraid.

He strokes his face with a handful of yellow flowers

Et se coupe devant lui une main sans qu'il y ait une goutte de
    rouge.
La main est tombée dans le sable où elle fond sans un soupir,
Une autre main toute pareille a pris sa place et les doigts
    bougent.

Et le noyé s'étonne de pouvoir monter à cheval,
De tourner la tête à droite et à gauche comme s'il était au pays
    natal,
Comme s'il y avait alentour une grande plaine, la liberté,
Et la permission d'allonger la main pour cueillir un fruit de
    l'été.

Est-ce donc la mort cela, cette rôdeuse douceur
Qui s'en retourne vers nous par une obscure faveur?

Et serais-je ce noyé chevauchant parmi les algues
Qui voit comme se reforme le ciel tourmenté de fables.

Je tâte mon corps mouillé comme un témoignage faible
Et ma monture hennit pour m'assurer que c'est elle.

Un berceau bouge, l'on voit un pied d'enfant réveillé.
Je m'en vais sous un soleil qui semble frais inventé.

Alentour il est des gens qui me regardent à peine,
Visages comme sur terre, mais l'eau a lavé leurs peines.

Et voici venir à moi des paisibles environs
Les bêtes de mon enfance et de la Création

Et le tigre me voit tigre, le serpent me voit serpent,
Chacun reconnaît en moi son frère, son revenant.

And cuts off one of his hands without a trace of blood.
The hand has fallen into the sand where it disappears without
    a sigh,
Another hand exactly the same has taken its place and the
    fingers are working.

And the drowned man is astonished because he can ride a
    horse
And turn his head to right and left as though he were in his
    native land,
As though a great plain stretched all around, and freedom,
And he could put out his hand and take a fruit from the
    summer trees.

Can this be death, this pleasant roaming
That brings us to ourselves again, by a mysterious favor?

And can I be that drowned man on horseback riding among
    the algae
Watching how the fabulous tormented sky becomes itself again.

I feel my wet body for evidence, however slight,
And my steed whinnies to assure me that it is he.

A cradle moves, the awakened infant shows a foot.
I go out under a sun that seems to have only just been
    invented.

All around are people who scarcely look at me,
Faces like those on earth, but the water has washed away
    their sorrows.

And there come to me from the peaceful country round
The animals of my childhood and the Creation.

And the tiger sees in me a tiger, and the snake a snake,
Each one recognizes in me his brother, his revenant.

Et l'abeille me fait signe de m'envoler avec elle
Et le lièvre qu'il connaît un gîte au creux de la terre

Où l'on ne peut pas mourir.

MONTEVIDEO

Je naissais, et par la fenêtre
Passait une fraîche calèche.

Le cocher réveillait l'aurore
D'un petit coup de fouet sonore.

Flottait un archipel nocturne
Encore sur le jour liquide.

Les murs s'éveillaient et le sable
Qui dort écrasé dans les murs.

Un peu de mon âme glissait
Sur un rail bleu, à contre-ciel,

Et un autre peu se mêlant
A un bout de papier volant

Puis, trébuchant sur une pierre,
Gardait sa ferveur prisonnière.

Le matin comptait ses oiseaux
Et jamais il ne se trompait.

And the bee gives me a sign to fly away with her
And the hare that he knows a hiding place hollowed in the
　　earth

Where you cannot die.

[J.K.]

MONTEVIDEO

I was born, and through my window
Rattled a frail barouche.

The coachman was making the daylight skip
With the flourish and crack of his sonorous whip.

An archipelago of dark
Floated still on the limpid day.

The walls woke up, the sands did too,
That sleep inside them, out of view.

Part of my soul began to slide
On a beam of blue against the sky.

And another small piece later
Got mixed with a slip of flying paper,

But, stumbling on a pebble,
Kept its pristine fervor well.

The day was counting up its birds
And never got the answer wrong.

Le parfum de l'eucalyptus
Se fiait à l'air étendu.

Dans l'Uruguay sur l'Atlantique
L'air était si liant, facile,
Que les couleurs de l'horizon
S'approchaient pour voir les maisons.

C'était moi qui naissais jusqu'au fond sourd des bois
Où tardent à venir les pousses
Et jusque sous la mer où l'algue se retrousse
Pour faire croire au vent qu'il peut descendre là.

La Terre allait, toujours recommençant sa ronde,
Reconnaissant les siens avec son atmosphère,
Et palpant sur la vague ou l'eau douce profonde
La tête des nageurs et les pieds des plongeurs.

MATHEMATIQUES

A Maria Blanchard

Quarante enfants dans une salle,
Un tableau noir et son triangle,
Un grand cercle hésitant et sourd
Son centre bat comme un tambour.

Des lettres sans mots ni patrie
Dans une attente endolorie.

Le parapet dur d'un trapèze,
Une voix s'élève et s'apaise

The scent of eucalyptus
Spread itself upon the air.

In Uruguay on the Atlantic
The air was so easy and so warm
That the colors of the horizon came
To look into the houses.

It was I who was being born, down to the deepest woods
Where the shoots are late in coming
And even down to undersea where the seaweeds wave
To make the wind believe it can blow down there.

The Earth went on in her ceaseless rolling,
Spreading her atmospheres to greet her children,
And feeling on the wave or the sweet deep water
The heads of swimmers and the feet of divers.

                                              [J.K.]

MATHEMATICS

                                    To Maria Blanchard

Forty children in a hall,
Blackboard, set-square on the wall,
A circle, big and blank and dumb,
Its center beating like a drum.

Letters without words or sense
Waiting in a hurt suspense.

Hard parapet-trapezium,
A voice is raised, and then is dumb;

Et le problème furieux
Se tortille et se mord la queue.

La mâchoire d'un angle s'ouvre.
Est-ce une chienne? Est-ce une louve?

Et tous les chiffres de la terre,
Tous ces insectes qui défont
Et qui refont leur fourmilière
Sous les yeux fixes des garçons.

TIGES

A Francis de Miomandre

Un peuplier sous les étoiles
Que peut-il.
Et l'oiseau dans le peuplier
Rêvant, la tête sous l'exil
Tout proche et lointain de ses ailes,
Que peuvent-ils tous les deux
Dans leur alliance confuse
De feuillages et de plumes
Pour gauchir la destinée.
Le silence les protège
Et le cercle de l'oubli
Jusqu'au moment où se lèvent
Le soleil, les souvenirs.
Alors l'oiseau de son bec

The problem, with an angry wail,
Twists and turns and bites its tail.

An angle opens wide its maw.
Is it a dog's or a wolf's sharp jaw?

We've all the numbers in the world,
All like insects that unbuild
And then build up their anthill maze
While on them children fix their gaze.

[J.K.]

STEMS

A poplar tree under the stars,
what can it do.
And the bird in the poplar tree
dreaming, his head
tucked into
far-and-near exile under his wing—
what can either of them
in their confused alliance of
leaves and feathers
do to avert destiny?

Silence and the
ring of forgetting
protect them until the moment when
the sun rises
and memory with it.
Then the bird

Coupe en lui le fil du songe
Et l'arbre déroule l'ombre
Qui va le garder tout le jour.

HIER ET AUJOURD'HUI

Toute la forêt attend que la statue abaisse son bras levé.
Ce sera pour aujourd'hui.
Hier on avait pensé que ce serait peut-être pour hier.
Aujourd'hui on en est sûr, même les racines le saven
Ce sera pour aujourd'hui.

POINTE DE FLAMME

Tout le long de sa vie
Il avait aimé à lire
Avec une bougie
Et souvent il passait

breaks with his beak the thread
of dream within him,
and the tree unrolls
the shadow that will guard it
throughout the day.

[D.L.]

YESTERDAY AND TODAY

All the forest is waiting for the statue to lower its raised arm.
Today it will happen.
Yesterday it was thought that perhaps it would happen
    yesterday.
Today it is certain, even the roots know it.
It will happen today.

[D.L.]

POINT OF FLAME

All his life long
he had loved to read by
candlelight
and often
    he would

La main dessus la flamme
Pour se persuader
Qu'il vivait,
Qu'il vivait.

Depuis le jour de sa mort
Il tient à côté de lui
Une bougie allumée
Mais garde les mains cachées.

400 ATMOSPHERES

A R. Guiraldes

Quand le groseillier qui pousse au fond des mers
Loin de tous les yeux regarde mûrir ses groseilles
Et les compare dans son cœur,
Quand l'eucalyptus des abîmes
A cinq mille mètres liquides médite un parfum sans espoir,
Des laboureurs phosphorescents glissent vers les moissons aqua-
        tiques,
D'autres cherchent le bonheur avec leurs paumes mouillées
Et la couleur de leurs enfants encore opaques
Qui grandissent sans se découvrir
Entre les algues et les perles.

pass his hand through the flame
to persuade himself that he
was alive,
he was alive.

Since the day of his death
he keeps beside him
a lit candle
but hides his hands.

[D.L.]

DEPTH 400 ATMOSPHERES

When the gooseberry bush that grows in the deep sea
watches its gooseberries ripen far from all eyes
and measures them in its heart,

when the eucalyptus of the abyss
three thousand fathoms down
meditates without hope
on a sweet scent,

the phosphorescent laborers glide to the watery harvest-fields.

And others
go with wet palms in search of joy,
seeking the color of their still opaque children,
who grow up without revealing themselves
among seaweed and pearls.

L'amour s'élance à travers les masses salines tombantes
Et la joie est évasive comme la mélancolie.
L'on pénètre comme à l'église sous les cascades de ténèbres
Qui ne font écume ni bruit.
Parfois on devine que passe un nuage venu du ciel libre
Et le dirige, rênes en main, une grave enfant de la côte.
Alors s'allument un à un les phares des profondeurs
Qui sont violemment plus noirs que la noirceur
Et tournent.

HAUTE MER

A Maurice Guillaume

Parmi les oiseaux et les lunes
Qui hantent le dessous des mers
Et qu'on devine à la surface
Aux folles phases de l'écume,

Parmi l'aveugle témoignage
Et les sillages sous-marins

Love
flashes across the
        falling saline masses

and joy is evasive as
          melancholy.
One enters it as if entering
a church under cascades of shadows
noiseless and foamless.

Sometimes it is divined that a cloud, come from the free sky,
is passing,
and some child of the shore, taking its bridle in hand,
gravely leads it along.
Then one by one
the deep-sea beacons light up,
violently blacker than blackness,
and swing their beams.

                         [D.L.]

DEEP SEA

Among the birds and moons that haunt
the sea depths

        presences
        evinced at the surface by
        strange gestures of foam,

blindly witnessed among their
underwater wakes by a thousand

Des mille poissons sans visage
Qui cachent en eux leur chemin,
Le noyé cherche la chanson
Où s'était formé son jeune âge,
Écoute en vain les coquillages
Et les fait choir au sombre fond.

DEPART

Un paquebot dans sa chaudière
Brûle les chaînes de la terre.

Mille émigrants sur les trois ponts
N'ont qu'un petit accordéon.

On hisse l'ancre, dans ses bras
Une sirène se débat

Et plonge en mer si offensée
Qu'elle ne se voit pas blessée.

Grandit la voix de l'Océan
Qui rend les désirs transparents.

Les mouettes font diligence
Pour qu'on avance, qu'on avance.

Le large monte à bord, pareil
A un aveugle aux yeux de sel.

faceless fishes, their
ongoing roads concealed in water,

the drowned man seeks for that song
his youth took form in,
listens in vain to shells
and lets them
drop to the
dark sea-floor.

[D.L.]

DEPARTURE

A liner in its fiery berth
Burns away the chains of earth.

The thousand emigrants have but one small
Accordion among them all.

The anchor's hoisted, on each arm
A mermaid wriggles with alarm,

Jumps back into the ocean, so astounded,
She's not aware of being wounded.

The ocean's voices high and higher
Swell, illuminating our desire.

The seagulls flurry to and fro
To wave us on, and on we go.

The high seas come on board, disguised
As blind men with briny eyes.

Dans l'espace avide, il s'élève
Lentement au mât de misaine.

PONT SUPERIEUR

Plante verte sur le pont,
Plante qui changes d'étoiles
Et vas d'escale en escale.
Goûtant à chaque horizon,

Plante, branches et ramilles,
L'hélice te fait trembler
Et ma main qui te dessine
Tremble d'être sur la mer.

Mais je découvre la terre
Prise dans ton pot carré
Celle-là que je cherchais
Dans le fond de ma jumelle.

AGE DES CAVERNES

A P. Figari

Les arbres se livrent peu à peu à leurs branches, penchant vers
leur couleur et poussent en tous sens des feuilles pour se gagner
les murmures de l'air. Ils respectent comme des dieux leurs

And in the gulf of space, at last
They slowly climb the mizzenmast.

[J.K.]

A POT OF EARTH

Green plant on shipboard, changing
with changing stars, plying
from port to port
                    you taste
every horizon

the propeller makes you
tremble from root to branch to
uttermost tendril
and my hand drawing you trembles at being
out at sea

but I discover
the earth set in your square pot
is the same earth I looked for
at the far end of my telescope.

[D.L.]

AGE OF CAVERNS

The trees deliver themselves little by little into their branches,
lean towards their color and push their leaves in all directions
to reach the murmuring of the air. Their reflections in the

images dans les étangs où tombent parfois des feuilles sacrifiées.

Les racines se demandent s'il faut ainsi s'accoupler au sol. Au milieu de la nuit l'une sort de terre pour écouter les étoiles et trembler.

La mer entend un bruit merveilleux et ignore en être la cause.

Les poissons qui se croisent feignent de ne pas se voir. Puis se cherchent durant des siècles.

Les rivières s'étonnent d'emporter toujours le ciel au fond de leur voyage et que le ciel les oublie.

Le ciel ne pose qu'une patte sur l'horizon, l'autre restant en l'air, immobile, dans une attente circulaire.

Tout le jour la lumière essaie des plumages différents et parfois, au milieu de la nuit, dans l'insomnie des couleurs.

La terre se croit une forêt, une montagne, un caillou, un souvenir. Elle a peur de l'horizon et craint de se disperser, de se trahir, de se tourner le dos. La nuit, le corps le long des corps, les visages près des visages, les fronts touchant les fronts, pour que les rêves se prêtent main-forte. L'âme bourdonne et s'approche pour voir comment bat un cœur dans le sommeil. Elle confond les étoiles avec les grillons et les cigales. Elle aime le soleil qui n'ose pas pénétrer dans les cavernes et se couche comme un chien devant le seuil.

On reconnaît les songes de chacun au dessin des paupières endormies.

Passent des animaux précédés d'un cou immense qui sonde l'inconnu, l'écartant à droite et à gauche, avec le plus grand soin. Ils défrichent l'air vierge.

Sans en parler aux autres insectes les fourmis montent sur la cime des arbres pour regarder.

Quand des tribus se rencontrent on se souffle au visage comme font les buffles qui se voient pour la première fois. On se regarde de tout près jusqu'à ce que les regards mettent le feu aux yeux. Alors on recule et on se saute à la gorge.

Les animaux se demandent lequel parmi eux sera l'homme un

ponds—into which from time to time sacrificial leaves drop down—they look upon as gods.

The roots ask themselves if they needs must be thus coupled to the soil. In the middle of the night a root issues from the earth to listen to the stars and to tremble.

The ocean hears a marvelous sound and does not know that it is its own voice.

Passing fishes pretend not to have seen one another. Then they search for each other through the centuries.

Rivers are astonished that they always carry the sky in the depths of their journeying and that the sky forgets them.

The sky puts just one paw on the horizon; the other remains in the air, motionless, in curved expectancy.

All day the light tries on different kinds of plumage, and sometimes, in the insomnia of colors, at night also.

The earth believes itself a forest, a mountain, a pebble, a memory. It is afraid of the horizon, afraid of scattering itself, betraying itself, afraid of turning its back on itself. At night body lies close to body, face to face, brow touching brow, so that dreams will come to the aid of dreams. The soul hums and draws near to see how a heart beats during sleep. It confuses the stars with grasshoppers and crickets. It loves the sun which dares not go inside the caves and lies down like a dog at the doorsill.

Each dreamer's dream can be recognized by the pattern of the sleeping eyelids.

Some animals pass by preceded by an immense neck which feels out the unknown, pushing it aside to left and right with the greatest care. They drive furrows through the virgin air. Without speaking of it to the other insects the ants climb to the treetops to look out.

When the tribes encounter one another they snuff at each others' faces like buffaloes meeting for the first time. They look at each other very closely until gazing sets fire to their eyes. Then they draw back and spring at each others' throats.

The animals wonder which among them will some day be man.

jour. Ils consultent l'horizon et le vent qui vient de l'avenir.
Ils pensent que peut-être l'homme rampe déjà dans l'herbe et
les regarde tour à tour présumant de leur chair et de son goût.
L'homme se demande si vraiment ce sera lui.

COEUR

A Pilar

Il ne sait pas mon nom
Ce cœur dont je suis l'hôte,
Il ne sait rien de moi
Que des régions sauvages.
Hauts plateaux faits de sang,
Épaisseurs interdites,
Comment vous conquérir
Sans vous donner la mort?
Comment vous remonter,
Rivières de ma nuit
Retournant à vos sources
Rivières sans poissons
Mais brûlantes et douces.
Je tourne autour de vous
Et ne puis aborder,
Bruîts de plages lointaines,
O courants de ma terre
Vous me chassez au large
Et pourtant je suis vous,
Et je suis vous aussi
Mes violents rivages,
Écumes de ma vie.

They consult the horizon and the wind that blows from the future. They think that perhaps man is already creeping among the grasses, and is looking at them each in turn, speculating about their flesh and its flavor. Man wonders if he himself really will be man.

[D.L.]

MY HEART

To Pilar

He does not know my name,
This heart housed within me,
He is aware only
Of my darkest regions.
High plateaux of my blood,
Impenetrable walls,
How shall I be able
To vanquish you, and live?
How shall I re-ascend
You, rivers of my night,
Returning to your source,
Rivers without a star,
But running fiery-sweet?
I sail from shore to
Far-distant-sounding shore,
And cannot disembark.
O my Earth, your currents
Thrust me far out to sea,
Yet I am part of you,
And I am you, also,
You tempestuous coasts,
Foaming sands of my life.

Beau visage de femme,
Corps entouré d'espace,
Comment avez-vous fait,
Allant de place en place,
Pour entrer dans cette île
Où je n'ai pas d'accès
Et qui m'est chaque jour
Plus sourde et insolite,
Pour y poser le pied
Comme en votre demeure,
Pour avancer la main
Comprenant que c'est l'heure
De prendre un livre ou bien
De fermer la croisée.
Vous allez, vous venez,
Vous prenez votre temps
Comme si vous suiviaient
Seuls les yeux d'un enfant.

Sous la voûte charnelle
Mon cœur qui se croit seul
S'agite prisonnier
Pour sortir de sa cage.
Si je pouvais un jour
Lui dire sans langage
Que je forme le cercle
Tout autour de sa vie!
Par mes yeux bien ouverts
Faire descendre en lui
La surface du monde
Et tout ce qui dépasse,
Les vagues et les cieux,
Les têtes et les yeux!
Ne saurais-je du moins
L'éclaire à demi
D'une mince bougie

O lovely woman's face,
And body clothed in space,
How, in your wanderings,
Did you discover this
Island that is closed to me,
And that becomes daily
More strange and more remote?
How were you able to
Set foot upon it, walk
In, as if it were your home;
To reach out with both hands,
Knowing it was time,
And take a book, or close
The open window?
You go from room to room
Calmly and leisurely
As if you were followed by
No more than a child's gentle gaze.

Under the dome of flesh
My heart, that a prison's
Solitude makes restless,
Struggles to free himself.
If some day, in simple terms,
I might only tell him
That I form the boundary
Which circumscribes his life!
Through my wide-opened eyes
Let him be penetrated
By the world's bright surface,
And all that moves upon it,
The oceans and the skies,
The faces, and the eyes!
With my slender candle
Could I not at least
Half-illuminate him,

Et lui montrer dans l'ombre
Celle qui vit en lui
Sans s'étonner jamais.

SAISIR

Saisir, saisir le soir, la pomme et la statue,
Saisir l'ombre et le mur et le bout de la rue.

Saisir le pied, le cou de la femme couchée
Et puis ouvrir les mains. Combien d'oiseaux lâchés

Combien d'oiseaux perdus qui deviennent la rue,
L'ombre, le mur, le soir, la pomme et la statue.

Mains, vous vous userez
A ce grave jeu-là
Il faudra vous couper
Un jour, vous couper ras.

Ce souvenir que l'on cache dans ses bras, à travers la fumée et
les cris,
Comme une jeune femme échappée à l'incendie,
Il faudra bien l'étendre dans le lit blanc de la mémoire, aux
rideaux tirés,
Et le regarder avec attention.
Que personne n'entre dans la chambre!
Il y a là maintenant un grand corps absolument nu

Show him in the shadow
The shade that lives in him,
And never is surprised?

[J.K.]

SEIZE

Seize, seize the apple and the statue and the night
Seize the shadow and the wall and the end of the street

Seize the foot, the neck of the lady in bed
Then open your hands. How many birds released

How many lost birds that turn into the street,
The shadow, the wall, the apple, the statue and the night?

Hands, you will wear yourselves out
At this dangerous game.
You will have to be cut
Off, one day, off at the wrist.

This memory we hide in our arms in the midst of the smoke
    and the shouting,
Like a young woman rescued from the flames,
Will have to be laid in the white bed of remembrance, with
    the curtains drawn,
And carefully considered.
Let no one enter the room!
A great body absolutely naked lies there now

Et une bouche qu'on croyait à jamais muette
Et qui soupire: "Amour", avec les lèvres mêmes de la vérité.

Grands yeux dans ce visage,
Qui vous a placés là?
De quel vaisseau sans mâts
Êtes-vous l'équipage?

Depuis quel abordage
Attendez-vous ainsi
Ouverts toute la nuit?

Feux noirs d'un bastingage
Étonnés mais soumis
A la loi des orages.

Prisonniers des mirages,
Quand sonnera minuit
Baissez un peu les cils
Pour reprendre courage.

Vous avanciez vers lui, femme des grandes plaines,
Nœud sombre de désir, distances au soleil.

Et vos lèvres soudain furent prises de givre
Quand son visage lent s'est approché de vous.

Vous parliez, vous parliez, des mots blafards et nus
S'en venaient jusqu'à lui, mille mots de statue.

Vous fîtes de cet homme une maison de pierre,
Une lisse façade aveugle nuit et jour.

And a mouth that we believed forever dumb
Whispering: "Love," with the very lips of truth.

Great eyes within this face, who
Placed you there?
Of what vessel with masts of air
Are you the crew?

Who boarded your decks,
That you must ride
The darkness, open wide?

Black flares on the bulwarks,
Astonished, you complied
With the law of storms and wrecks.

Prisoners of a mirage,
When the strokes of midnight settle,
Lower your lids a little
To give yourself courage.

You were moving towards him, woman of the great plains,
A dark binding-together of sun and distance and desire.

And your lips were suddenly seized with frost
When his slow face began to come towards you.

You were speaking, speaking, and ghostly, naked words
Wavered towards him, the words of a statue, numberless.

You made of that man a house of stone,
A featureless façade, unseeing day and night.

Ne peut-il dans ses murs creuser une fenêtre,
Une porte laissant faire six pas dehors?

Saisir quand tout me quitte,
Et avec quelles mains
Saisir cette pensée,
Et avec quelles mains
Saisir enfin le jour
Par la peau de son cou,
Le tenir remuant
Comme un lièvre vivant?
Viens, sommeil, aide-moi,
Tu saisiras pour moi
Ce que je n'ai pu prendre,
Sommeil aux mains plus grandes.

★

Dans la chambre où je fus rêvait un long lézard
Qu'embrasait un soleil ignoré par le ciel,
Des oiseaux traversaient le haut toit sans le voir,
Je me croyais masqué par mon propre secret.

Des visages nouveaux formés par le hasard
Riaient et sans que l'on perçût le moindre rire.
L'air était naturel mais il était sans bruit,
Tout semblait vivre au fond d'un insistant regard.

Comme se dévoilait l'épaule d'une femme,
Un homme qui sortit d'un pan profond du mur
Me dit en approchant son corps plus que son âme:
"Comment avez-vous fait pour venir jusqu'ici,

Votre visage est nu comme une main qui tremble.

May he not let a single window into his walls,
And an open door, that will let him step outside a little?

Seize when all else fails me,
And with what hands
May I seize that thought,
And with what hands
Seize, at last, the daylight
By the scruff of the neck,
And hold it wriggling
Like a live hare?
Come, sleep, and help me,
You shall seize for me
What I could not hold,
Sleep, in your larger hands.

★

In the room where I was working a long lizard lay dreaming,
Basking in a sun the sky knew nothing of,
Birds went flashing through the roof as if it was not there.
And I believed myself covered by a mask of secrecy!

New faces, features formed by accident,
Laughed, though without the slightest noise.
The air was natural but without sound,
Everything seemed to be living under one persistent gaze.

As a woman's shoulder began revealing itself,
A man who was emerging from a blank space in the wall
Addressed me, bringing his body nearer than his soul:
"How did you manage to come all this way,

Your face is as naked as a trembling hand.

Vous avez beau cacher vos yeux et vos genoux.
Chacun vous vit entrer et nul ne vous ressemble,
Allez-vous-en, le jour même, ici, vous déroute

Et rien entre ces murs jamais ne songe à vous."

EN PAYS ETRANGER

Ces visages sont-ils venus de ma mémoire,
Et ces gestes ont-ils touché terre ou le ciel?
Cet homme est-il vivant comme il semble le croire,
Avec sa voix, avec cette fumée aux lèvres?
Chaises, tables, bois dur, vous que je peux toucher
Dans ce pays neigeux dont je ne sais la langue,
Poêle, et cette chaleur qui chuchote à mes mains,
Quel est cet homme devant vous qui me ressemble
Jusque dans mon passé, sachant ce que je pense,
Touchant si je vous touche et comblant mon silence,
Et qui soudain se lève, ouvre la porte, passe
En laissant tout ce vide où je n'ai plus de place?

Tendez la main, touchez ces grands monts invisibles
Cet homme vous apporte en cette chambre close
Un peu du ciel qui rôde au-dessus des montagnes.
Rafraîchissez vos mains à ses rives mouvantes,
Penchez-vous et voyez comme le parquet même
Est un lac doux et triste où tremble votre image.

You need not try to hide your eyes and your knees,
Everyone saw you come in and there is no one like you.
Go away now, for here the light of day disconcerts you,

And there is nothing within these walls that ever thinks
  of you."

[J.K.]

IN A FOREIGN LAND

Did these faces rise out of my memory
And did these gestures touch the heavens or the earth?
Is this man alive who appears to think he is,
With his voice speaking, and that breath coming from his lips?
Chairs, tables, solid wood, you whom I can touch
In this snowy country whose language I do not know,
You, fire, whose ardor whispers to my hands:
Who is this man before you who copies me
Down to each detail even of my former life, my present
  thought?
Who, if I go to touch you, touches you also, making good my
  silence,
And who suddenly gets up, opens the door, and goes
Leaving all this emptiness where I can have no place?

Put out your hand, and touch those high, invisible peaks
That this man brings into your shuttered room
With a little of the sky that floats above the mountains.
Cool your hands in his moving waters.
Bend down, and see how the floor itself
Is a sad and quiet lake in which your image trembles.

[J.K.]

Dans la forêt sans heures
On abat un grand arbre.
Un vide vertical
Tremble en forme de fût
Près du tronc étendu.

Cherchez, cherchez, oiseaux,
La place de vos nids
Dans ce haut souvenir
Tant qu'il murmure encore.

LES CHEVAUX DU TEMPS

Quand les chevaux du Temps s'arrêtent à ma porte
J'hésite un peu toujours à les regarder boire
Puisque c'est de mon sang qu'ils étanchent leur soif.
Ils tournent vers ma face un œil reconnaissant
Pendant que leurs longs traits m'emplissent de faiblesse
Et me laissent si las, si seul et décevant
Qu'une nuit passagère envahit mes paupières
Et qu'il me faut soudain refaire en moi des forces
Pour qu'un jour où viendrait l'attelage assoiffé
Je puisse encore vivre et les désaltérer.

IN THE FOREST

In the timeless forest
A high tree is felled.
An upright void
Trembles, shaped like a trunk,
Beside the fallen tree.

While it still is murmuring,
Seek, birds, seek
Where your nests once rested
In this lofty memory.

[J.K.]

THE HORSES OF TIME

When the horses of Time are halted at my door
I am always a little afraid to watch them drink
Since it is with my blood they quench their thirst.
They turn upon me a look of recognition
And I am overwhelmed with weakness from their lengthy
    draughts.
They leave me so weary, so elusive and alone
That an interval of dusk descends upon my eyelids
And I must suddenly build up my strength again
So that each day the thirsty creatures come
I can be still alive, and slake their thirst.

[J.K.]

L'OISEAU

Oiseau, que cherchez-vous, voletant sur mes livres,
Tout vous est étranger dans mon étroite chambre.

—J'ignore votre chambre et je suis loin de vous,
Je n'ai jamais quitté mes bois, je suis sur l'arbre
Où j'ai caché mon nid, comprenez autrement
Tout ce qui vous arrive, oubliez un oiseau.

—Mais je vois de tout près vos pattes, votre bec.

—Sans doute pouvez-vous rapprocher les distances
Si vos yeux m'ont trouvé ce n'est pas de ma faute.

—Pourtant vous êtes là puisque vous répondez.

—Je réponds à la peur que j'ai toujours de l'homme
Je nourris mes petits, je n'ai d'autre loisir,
Je les garde en secret au plus sombre d'un arbre
Que je croyais touffu comme l'un de vos murs.
Laissez-moi sur ma branche et gardez vos paroles,
Je crains votre pensée comme un coup de fusil.

—Calmez donc votre cœur qui m'entend sous la plume.

—Mais quelle horreur cachait votre douceur obscure
Ah! vous m'avez tué je tombe de mon arbre.

—J'ai besoin d'être seul, même un regard d'oiseau...

—Mais puisque j'étais loin au fond de mes grands bois!

THE BIRD

Bird, what are you seeking, flying over my books,
All is foreign to you in my narrow room.

—I do not know your room and I am far from you,
I have never left my woods, I am on the tree
Where I have concealed my nest. Find some other explanation
For all that happens to you now, bird must be forgotten.

—But I can see your beak, your claws, quite close to me.

—You can doubtless bring the distances together
If your eyes have found me, it is no fault of mine.

—But you are there, since you answer me.

—I answer the fear that I always have of man
I feed my little ones, I have no other privilege,
I hide them away in the darkest part of the tree
Which I thought was as thick as one of your walls.
Leave me alone on my branch and keep your words to yourself,
I am afraid of your thoughts as of a pistol shot.

—Be still, heart, that listens to me underneath its plumage.

—But what horror hid behind your obscure gentleness
Oh! You have killed me I fall from my tree.

—I need to be alone, even a bird's eye . . .

—But when I was far away in the depths of my great woods!

[J.K.]

L'OURS

Le pôle est sans soupirs.
Un ours tourne et retourne
Une boule plus blanche
Que la neige et que lui.
Comment lui faire entendre
Du fond de ce Paris
Que c'est l'ancienne sphère
De plus en plus réduite
D'un soleil de minuit,
Quand cet ours est si loin
De cette chambre close,
Qu'il est si différent
Des bêtes familières
Qui passent à ma porte,
Ours penché sans comprendre
Sur son petit soleil
Qu'il voudrait peu à peu
Réchauffer de son souffle
Et de sa langue obscure
Comme s'il le prenait
Pour un ourson frileux
Qui fait le mort en boule
Et ferme fort les yeux.

FIGURES

Je bats comme des cartes
Malgré moi des visages.

BEAR

At the breathless Pole
A bear is turning round and round
A ball whiter
Than snow and as shining.
How can you make him understand
From the depths of this Paris
That this is an old globe,
Ever more and more reduced,
Of a midnight sun.
The bear is so far away
From this closed room.
He is so different
From the familiar beasts
Who pass my door.
The bear uncomprehending, bends over
His little sun
And tries, bit by bit,
To warm it with his breath
And his dark tongue.
As if he took it
For another chilly bear
Dying inside the ball,
With tight closed eyes.

                                        [K.R.]

FACES

In spite of myself
I deal the faces
As if they were cards,

Et, tous, ils me sont chers.
Parfois l'un tombe à terre
Et j'ai beau le chercher
La carte a disparu.
Je n'en sais rien de plus.
C'était un beau visage
Pourtant, que j'aimais bien.
Je bats les autres cartes.
L'inquiet de ma chambre,
Je veux dire mon cœur,
Continue à brûler
Mais non pour cette carte,
Qu'une autre a remplacée:
C'est un nouveau visage,
Le jeu reste complet
Mais toujours mutilé.
C'est tout ce que je sais,
Nul n'en sait davantage.

POUR UN POETE MORT

Donnez-lui vite une fourmi
Et si petite soit-elle,
Mais qu'elle soit bien à lui!
Il ne faut pas tromper un mort.
Donnez-la lui, ou bien le bec d'une hirondelle,
Un bout d'herbe, un bout de Paris,
Il n'a plus qu'un grand vide à lui
Et comprend encor mal son sort.

And they all are dear to me.
Sometimes one falls to the ground
And I seek for it in vain—
The card has disappeared.
I know no more about it,
And yet, it was a lovely face
That I loved well.
I deal the other cards.
In my room the unquiet one,
I mean my heart,
Goes on burning
But not for that card
Which another has replaced:
It is another face,
The pack is still complete
Yet spoiled now for always.
That is all I know,
No one knows any more.

[J.K.]

FOR A DEAD POET

Quick, give him an ant
No matter how tiny,
But let it be his very own!
You must not cheat the dead.
Let it be his own! Or else a swallow's beak,
A blade of grass, a fraction of Paris;
He has nothing left but his own great emptiness
And comprehends his fate imperfectly as yet.

A choisir il vous donne en échange
Des cadeaux plus obscurs que la main ne peut prendre:
Un reflet qui couche sous la neige,
Ou l'envers du plus haut des nuages,
Le silence au milieu du topage,
Ou l'étoile que rien ne protège.
Tout cela il le nomme et le donne
Lui qui est sans un chien ni personne.

La lampe rêvait tout haut qu'elle était l'obscurité
Et répandait alentour des ténèbres nuancées,
Le papier se brunissait sous son regard apaisé,
Les murs veillaient assourdis l'intimité sans limites.
S'il vous arrivait d'ouvrir des livres sur des rayons
Voilà qu'ils apparaissaient avec leur texte changé,
Et l'on voyait çà et là luire des mots chuchotants.
Vous déceliez votre nom en désarroi dans le texte
Et cependant que tombait une petite pluie d'ombres
Métamorphosant les mots sous un acide inconnu,
Un dormeur rêvait tout bas près de sa lampe allumée.

LE POIDS D'UNE JOURNEE

Solitude, tu viens armée d'êtres sans fin dans ma propre
    chambre:
Il pleut sur le manteau de celui-ci, il neige sur celui-là
    et cet autre est éclairé par le soleil de Juillet.

He gives you in exchange a choice
Of gifts more mysterious than the hand can seize:
A light reflected underneath the snow,
Or the far side of the highest clouds,
Silence in the midst of noise,
Or the star that nothing shelters.

All these he calls by name and gives in song,
He who has no dog, or anyone.

[J.K.]

The lamp was talking out loud in her sleep, dreaming she
    was the darkness,
And spread around her varying depths of shade.
The paper darkened, sobered by her tranquil gaze,
The walls without ears witnessed boundless intimacy.
If you happened to open a book under its rays,
They opened on an altered text,
And here and there could be seen glittering words that
    whispered.
You discovered your name scattered in disorder through the
    text;
And whilst a small shower of shadows fell
Altering the words with some undiscovered acid,
Someone dreaming beside his lighted lamp
Was talking softly in his sleep.

[J.K.]

THE BURDEN OF A SINGLE DAY

Solitude, into my own room you come, armed with countless
    beings:
There is rain on this one's coat, on his there is snow, and
    that one is lit by the sun of July.

Ils sortent de partout. "Écoutez-moi! Écoutez-moi!"
Et chacun voudrait en dire un peu plus que l'autre.
Il en est qui cherchent un frère disparu, d'autres, leur maî-
     tresse, leurs enfants.
"Je ne puis rien faire pour vous."
Ils ont tous un mot à dire avant de disparaître:
"Écoutez-moi, puisque je vous dis que je m'en irai aussitôt
     après."
Ils me font signe de m'asseoir pour que l'entretien soit
     plus long.
"Puisque je vous dis que je ne puis rien faire pour vous,
Fantômes pour les yeux et pour les oreilles!"
Il y a cet inconnu qui me demande pardon et disparaît
     sans que je connaisse son crime,
Cette jeune fille qui a traversé des bois qui ne sont pas
     de nos pays,
Cette vielle femme qui me demande conseil. "Conseil
     à quel sujet?"
Elle ne veut rien ajouter et se retire indignée.

Maintenant il n'y a plus dans la chambre que ma table
     allongée, mes livres, mes papiers.
Ma lampe éclaire une tête, des mains humaines,
Et mes lèvres se mettent à rêver pour leur propre compte
     comme des orphelines.

LUI SEUL

Si vous touchez sa main c'est bien sans le savoir,
Vous vous le rappelez mais sous un autre nom,
Au milieu de la nuit, au plus fort du sommeil,
Vous dites son vrai nom et le faites asseoir.

They come from everywhere: "Listen to me! Listen to me!"
And each one wants to be telling me more than the others.
There are some who are seeking a lost brother, and others their
    mistresses, their children.
"I can do nothing for you."
They all have something to tell me before they vanish away:
"Listen to me, and I promise I'll go away at once."
They make signs to me to sit down, so that their talk may
    last a little longer.
"But I've told you I can do nothing for you,
Phantasms of my eyes and of my ears!"
—There is that stranger who asks me to forgive him and then
    disappears before I have learned what his crime is;
That young girl who has wandered through woods that are not
    in our country;
And that old woman who asks my advice: "Advice on what
    subject?"
But she won't say another word and indignantly vanishes.

There is nothing now in this room of mine—only my long
    table, my books, my papers.
My lamp illuminates a head, and human hands,
And my lips begin to dream on their own, like lost children.

                         [J.K.]

HE ALONE

If you touch his hand it is quite without knowing.
You remember him, but he had another name.
In the middle of the night, in the depths of sleep,
You speak his real name and ask him to be seated.

Un jour on frappe et je devine que c'est lui
Qui s'en vient près de nous à n'importe quelle heure
Et vous le regardez avec un tel oubli
Qu'il s'en retourne au loin mais en laissant derrière

Une porte vivante et pâle comme lui.

ALTER EGO

Une souris s'échappe
(Ce n'en était pas une)
Une femme s'éveille
(Comment le savez-vous?)
Et la porte qui grince
(On l'huila ce matin)
Près du mur de clôture
(Le mur n'existe plus)
Ah! je ne puis rien dire
(Eh bien, vous vous tairez!)
Je ne puis pas bouger
(Vous marchez sur la route)
Où allons-nous ainsi?
(C'est moi qui le demande)
Je suis seul sur la Terre
(Je suis là près de vous)
Peut-on être si seul
(Je le suis plus que vous,
Je vois votre visage
Nul ne m'a jamais vu).

One day there comes a knock and I guess it is he
Who comes to be beside us at any time
And you give him such an empty stare
That he turns and goes far away, but leaving behind him

A living door, as pale as he himself.

                                                    [J.K.]

ALTER EGO

A mouse runs out
(It was not there)
A woman wakes
(How do you know?)
And the squeaking door
(It was oiled this morning)
Near the cloister wall
(There is now no wall)
Oh! I can't say a thing
(Well now you'll be quiet!)
I cannot move
(You're walking along the road)
Does all this get us anywhere?
(I'm asking you)
I'm alone on Earth
(I am here beside you)
Can one be so alone
(I am more alone than you,
I can see your face,
No one has ever seen mine.)

                                                    [J.K.]

LE CHAOS ET LA CREATION

(DIEU PARLE)

Je suis dans le noirceur et j'entends ma puissance
Faire un bruit sourd, battant l'espace rapproché,
Alentour un épais va-et-vient de distances
Me flaire, me redoute et demeure caché.
Je sens tout se creuser, ignorant de ses bornes,
Et puis tout se hérisse en ses aspérités.
Serais-je menacé par les flèches sans formes
De fantômes durcis dans de longs cauchemars.
Mais non, tout se précise en moi-même, je gagne!
Je suis déjà la plaine au delà du hasard
Et, haussant tout ce noir, je deviens la montagne
Et la neige nouvelle attendant sa couleur
Ah que ne sombre point la plus grande pâleur
La cime qui m'ignore et déjà m'accompagne
Et que je cesse enfin d'être mon inconnu.
Que la lumière soit . . .

Maintenant que j'ai mis partout de la lumière
Il me faudra pousser le ciel loin de la terre,
Et pour être bien sûr d'avoir tout mon espace
Je ferai que le vent et les nuages passent
Ainsi que les oiseaux qui viennent et qui vont
Vérifiant les airs, la surface, le fond.
Tout me supplie et veut une forme précise,
Tout a hâte de respirer dans sa franchise
Et voudrait se former dès que je le prévois,
Et ma tête foisonne, et mon être bourdonne
De milliers de silences, tous différents,
Ce sont les voix de ceux qui n'en ont pas encore
Et quémandent un nom pour aller de l'avant.

CHAOS AND CREATION

(GOD SPEAKS)

I am in darkness, and I listen to my forces
Making a hollow noise upon the drum of space.
Distance with distance industriously shuttling
Hovers around me, dreads me, and remains concealed.
I feel the All grow hollow, knowing no boundaries,
Then it stands erect and raises its rugged spine.
Can I be threatened by the shapeless arrowheads
Of phantoms become solid in the nightmare of time?
No! all things now take their shape through me—I cannot lose!
Already I am turning into the plain that is beyond all doubt,
And, hoisting all this blackness up, I am the mountain
And the freshly fallen snow that waits for its color.
Ah, let it sink not, that whitest of all whitenesses,
The peak that knows me not yet follows me already;
And let me cease to be a stranger to myself.
Let there be light . . .

Now that I have illuminated everything
I must push the sky far, far away from earth,
And to make quite sure that I still have all of space
I shall make the wind and the clouds pass in between
Just like the birds that come and go
Testing the surface and the depths of atmosphere.
Everything implores me to give it a definite shape
Everything hastens, in its innocence, to breathe,
And wants to see itself completed the moment I conceive
How it should look; my brain teems, and my whole being
    throbs
With a million million silences, no two alike: they are
The voices of those who do not yet possess a voice,
Demanding their names so that they can take their place

Chacun son tour, le temps viendra pour tous d'éclore.

Je vois clair, je vois noir et non pas que j'hésite,
L'un fera suite à l'autre et les deux si profonds
Que dans mon univers ils seront sans réplique
Et ce sera le jour et la nuit, l'horizon.
Je vois bleu et frangé de blanchissants détours,
Cela fuit sous mes yeux et si j'y trempe un doigt
C'est salé: cela va très loin et fait le tour
De la Terre et c'est plein d'écailleux très adroits,
C'est ce qu'on nommera la mer et les poissons,
A l'homme de trouver comment l'on va dessus,
Sans se laisser périr attiré par le fond
Ni le vent, grand pousseur de vagues et de nues.

Sombres troupeaux des monts sauvages, étagés,
Faites attention, vous allez vous figer.
Ne pouvant vous laisser errer à votre guise
Je m'en vais vous donner d'éternelles assises.
Les chamois bondiront pour vous. Quant aux nuages,
Libre à vous de les retenir à leur passage.
Vous ne bougerez plus, mais je vous le promets
Autour d'un pivot sûr toujours vous tournerez
Et les jours bougeront pour vous, mes immobiles,
Et les sources coulant de vos sommets tranquilles
Porteront l'altitude au long de leur chemin
En reflétant le ciel, spacieux riverain.

Je ne sais maintenant ce que je porte en moi,
Mes yeux font de l'obscur et je cherche à mieux voir,
J'ajuste mon regard, la chose se précise,
Elle n'a qu'un seul corps, une espèce de tronc,
Mais le ciel dans le haut en branches le divise

Among the first created things.
But each one in his turn: the time shall come for each one
   to be awakened.

I see light, see dark—not that I am unsure of myself—
The one shall follow on the other, and both so profound
That in my universe they shall not have their like,
And it shall be night and day, and the horizon.
I see blue surrounded by a fringe of whiteness,
It runs from my eyes and if I dip my finger in
It tastes of salt; it stretches far away and goes
Right round the Earth, is full of lively scaly things.
These are what shall be known as the sea and the fishes.
It is for Man to discover how to travel over it
Without perishing, dragged downwards by the deep
Or by the wind, great blower of billows.

You sombre, savage herds of towering mountains,
Take care, you are going to be fixed for ever.
As I cannot let you wander at your own sweet will
I shall provide you with perpetual foundations.
The chamois shall leap for you, and as for the clouds,
You have permission to detain them in their flight.
You shall never stir again, but I promise you
Shall turn upon the pivot of eternity,
And the daylight shall move for you, my unmoving ones,
And the springs that rush from your tranquil mountain tops
Shall carry in them all the way your lofty height
Reflected as the sky, whose spacious grounds lie at the river's
   edge.

I do not know what it is I carry in me now—
My eyes make darkness, I try to peer through it—
I focus my sight, and the thing becomes clearer,
It has only one body, a sort of trunk
But the sky at the top divides it into branches

Porteuses d'équilibre et de confusion,
Et je songe au plaisir de s'étendre dessous.
Arbres, venez à moi puisque je pense à vous!
Vous vous accrocherez à la terre fertile
Et ne ressemblerez à l'homme que par l'ombre,
Vous qui m'ignorerez de toutes vos racines
Et ne saurez de moi que le vol des colombes.

Parfois je ne sais rien de ce qui va venir
Et je vois devant moi quelque vieux souvenir
Devenu plante, ou pierre ou fraîcheur qui se pose,
Même ce que je fis, pensant à autre chose.
Cela tombe de moi comme un fruit oublié
Mais toujours reconnu et jamais renié.
Soudain je vois petit, cela porte un fardeau,
C'est noir, c'est courageux, l'une précédant l'autre,
Et le temps d'y penser, c'est déjà la fourmi;
Va ton chemin, je viens de te donner la vie.

Ivresse de créer, de tout voir aboutir,
De n'avoir pas à commencer et de finir,
De délivrer soudain les fleuves et les pierres,
Les cœurs battants, les yeux, les âmes prisonnières.
Tout m'échappe, les flots et les terres en vrac,
Mélange de courants, de vivantes folies,
Mais un de mes regards rend le calme d'un lac,
Préservant en dessous ce qu'il y faut de vie.
Que rien n'ait peur de vivre au sortir de mon corps,
Ni les petits poissons menacés dans leur fuite,
Ni les grands dévorés à leur tour par la mort
Ni tout ce qui remue et doute au fond du sort.
Tout me revient, trouvant en moi de la justice,
Prêt à se reformer dans mon clair précipice.

Bringing with them balance and disorder,
And I dream of the pleasure of lying in its shade.
Trees, come hither, since I bend my thoughts to you!
You shall attach yourselves to the fertile Earth
And only by your shadow shall you resemble Man,
You who in every root shall be unaware of my existence
And shall know of me nothing but the flight of doves.

Sometimes I know nothing of what is about to be born
And I see before me finally some old old memory
Become plant, or stone, or a coolness that lays itself
On earth, made all of them with my mind on other things.
They fall from me like forgotten fruits,
Yet I always remember them again, never disown them.
All at once I see something tiny, carrying
A load—it is black, courageous, one follows behind the other,
And before I have time to think, it is a real live ant:
Go your way, ant, I have just given you your life.

O̅ the bliss of creating, of seeing everything achieved,
Not to have to begin and to finish,
Suddenly to deliver the rivers and the rocks,
The beating hearts, the eyes, the captive soul.
All flows from me, the waters and the tumbled earth,
A crisscross of currents and animated extravagances:
But one look from my eyes gives it the calm of a lake,
With whatever life is needed carefully preserved.
Let nothing be afraid of living when it leaves my body,
Neither the little fishes that dart through the dangers of the
    deep,
Nor the big ones devoured in their turn by death,
Nor all things that move and in their hearts are doubtful of
    their fate.
All things return to me, and finding I am justice
Prepare to form themselves anew in my precipice of light.

Assez pour aujourd'hui, je suis las de créer,
Et je veux seulement dormir pour qu'il y ait
Beaucoup d'herbe, beaucoup d'herbages sur la terre,
De la broussaille qui ressemble a du sommeil,
A l'image de moi quand je reposerai.
Je pense même avoir quelque idée en dormant
Qui franchira le rève en sa hâte de vivre
Et ce sera la chèvre avec son bêlement,
Ou le poisson volant, ou quelque autre surprise,
Comme hier, quand je fus réveillé par la brise
Qui me halait à soi d'un fertile sommeil
Inquiète de voir ce que je pensais d'elle.

Emmêlé à tant d'étoiles,
Me dégageant peu à peu,
Je sens que poussent mes lois
Dans le désordre des cieux.
La solitude du monde
Et la mienne se confondent,
Ah! nul n'est plus seul que Dieu
Dans sa poitrine profonde.

Il faut que quelque part
Quelqu'un vive et respire
Et sans bien le savoir
Soit dans ma compagnie,
Qu'il sache dans son sein
Évasif que j'existe,
Qu'il me situe au loin
Et que je lui resiste,

Moi qui serai en lui.

Enough for one day—I am weary of creating
And I simply want to go to sleep, that there may be
Rich grass and many pastures on the earth,
And the deep underwoods that resemble slumber,
Made in the image of myself when I am resting.
I may even have some new idea while I am asleep
That will step out of my dream in its great hurry to be alive,
And it shall be the nanny-goat with her bleating,
Or the flying fish, or some other curiosity;
Just as yesterday, I was awakened by the breeze
That hauled me up out of a fertile slumber,
Anxious to know what I would have to say about her.

[J.K.]

Entangled in so many stars,
From which I gradually free myself,
I feel my laws take shape
In the disorder of the skies.
The earth's solitude
And my own are mingled.
Ah! none is more alone than God
In his heart's great pit.

Someone somewhere
Must live and breathe
And without quite realizing it
Be my companion:
Let him know in his heart
In spite of its evasions that I exist;
Let him set me up on high,
And let me not yield to him,

I who shall be in him forever.

[J.K.]

DIEU PENSE A L'HOMME

Il faudra bien qu'il me ressemble,
Je ne sais encore comment,
Moi qui suis les mondes ensemble
Avec chacun de leurs moments.
Je le veux séperer du reste
Et me l'isole dans les bras,
Je voudrais adopter ses gestes
Avant qu'il soit ce qu'il sera,
Je le devine à sa fenêtre
Mais la maison n'existe pas.
Je le tâte, je le tâtonne,
Je le forme sans le vouloir
Je me le donne, je me l'ôte,
Que je suis pressé de le voir!
Je le garde, je le retarde
Afin de le mieux concevoir.
Tantôt, informe, tu t'éloignes
Tu boites au fond de la nuit
Ou tu m'escalades, grandi,
Jusqu'à devenir un géant.
Moi que nul regard ne contrôle
Je te veux visible de loin,
Moi qui suis silence sans fin
Je te donnerai la parole,
Moi qui ne peux pas me poser
Je te veux debout sur tes pieds,
Moi qui suis partout à la fois
Je te veux mettre en un endroit,
Moi qui suis plus seul dans ma fable
Qu'un agneau perdu dans les bois,
Moi qui ne mange ni ne bois
Je veux t'asseoir à une table,

GOD THINKS OF MAN

He must resemble me,
I do not know just yet exactly how,
I who am all worlds entirely
With each moment of their time.
I will separate him from the rest
And isolate him in my arms,
I shall imitate his gestures
Before he becomes what he shall be,
I divine the presence at the window
But the house is not constructed yet.
I taste him, I test him,
I shape him unintentionally,
Give him to myself, and snatch him away.
How impatient I am to see him!
I guard him, I retard him
So as to conceive him better—
Sometimes, unformed, you step back
With a limp into the depths of night.
Or you climb upon me, growing larger
Till you have become a giant.
I whom no eye controls
Wish you to be visible from afar,
I who am silence without end
Shall give you speech,
I who cannot set my feet on anything
Wish to see you standing on your feet,
I who am everywhere at once
Wish to set you down upon a fixed spot,
I who am more lonely in my fable
Than the lamb lost in the forest,
I who can neither eat nor drink,
I want to seat you at a table

Une femme en face de toi,
Moi qui suis sans cesse suprême
Toujours ignorant le loisir,
Qui n'en peux mais avec moi-même
Puisque je ne peux pas finir,
Je veux que tu sois périssable,
Tu seras mortel, mon petit,
Je te coucherai dans le lit
De la terre où se font les arbres.

LE PREMIER ARBRE

C'était lors de mon premier arbre,
J'avais beau le sentir en moi
Il me surprit par tant de branches,
Il était arbre mille fois.
Moi qui suis tout ce que je forme
Je ne me savais pas feuillu,
Voilà que je donnais de l'ombre
Et j'avais des oiseaux dessus.
Je cachais ma sève divine
Dans ce fût qui montait au ciel
Mais j'étais pris par la racine
Comme à un piège naturel.
C'était lors de mon premier arbre,
L'homme s'assit sous le feuillage
Si tendre d'être si nouveau.
Était-ce un chêne ou bien un orme
C'est loin et je ne sais pas trop
Mais je sais bien qu'il plut à l'homme

With a woman facing you,
I who am supreme at all times,
Always without thought of leisure
Since I cannot be finished ever
Excepting my whole self come to an end,
I want you to be born to die,
You shall be mortal, my little one,
I shall lay you in the bed
Of earth from which the trees are sprung.

[J.K.]

THE FIRST TREE

It was the time of my very first tree.
I might as well never have felt it in me,
It surprised me so, it had so many branches.
It was tree a thousand and one times over.
I who am all that is conceived by me
Did not realize just how leafy I would be.
Here was I casting shadows on the ground
And in my crown there were birds.
My divine sap I concealed
In this trunk which mounted to the sky
But I was held by the roots
As in a trap contrived by Nature.
It was the time of my very first tree.
Man came and sat beneath its leaves
Which being fresh were also very delicate.
Was it an oak or could it have been an elm
It's so long ago I really couldn't say
But I know that Man was pleased with it

Qui s'endormit les yeux en joie
Pour y rêver d'un petit bois.
Alors au sortir de son somme
D'un coup je fis une forêt
De grands arbres nés centenaires
Et trois cents cerfs la parcouraient
Avec leurs biches déjà mères,
Ils croyaient depuis très longtemps
L'habiter et la reconnaître
Les six-cors et leurs bramements
Non loin de faons encore à naître.
Ils avaient, à peine jaillis,
Plus qu'il ne fallait d'espérance
Ils étaient lourds de souvenirs
Qui dans les miens prenaient naissance.
D'un coup je fis chênes, sapins,
Beaucoup d'écureuils pour les cîmes,
L'enfant qui cherche son chemin
Et le bûcheron qui l'indique,
Je cachai de mon mieux le ciel
Pour ses distances malaisées
Mais je le redonnai pour tel
Dans les oiseaux et la rosée.

TRISTESSE DE DIEU

(DIEU PARLE)

Je vous vois aller et venir sur le tremblement de la Terre
Comme aux premiers jours du monde, mais grande est
     la différence,
Mon œuvre n'est plus en moi, je vous l'ai toute donnée.

His eyes were shining when he fell asleep,
And dreamed that he was in a little wood,
So when he wakened from his slumber
I made a forest at a single stroke
With great trees born in their hundredth year
And three hundred deer roaming among them
With their hinds that were old enough already to be mothers.
The trees thought they had lived there
And known a long, long time
The forest, and the antlered stags that bellowed
To the young deer still unborn.
Scarcely had they sprung out of the earth
They were filled with aspirations
They were weighed down with their memories
Which had their roots in mine.
At a single stroke I made the oak, the pine,
With lots of squirrels for the topmost branches,
The little girl who has lost her way
And the woodcutter who directs her.
I did my best to cover up the sky
Because of its disturbing distances,
But I gave it back again
In birds and dew.

[J.K.]

GOD'S SADNESS

(GOD SPEAKS)

I can see you coming and going upon the trembling of the
      Earth
As in the world's first days, but with this great difference:
I labor no longer for myself, but for you entirely.

Hommes, mes bien-aimés, je ne puis rien dans vos malheurs,
Je n'ai pu que vous donner votre courage et les larmes,
C'est la preuve chaleureuse de l'existence de Dieu.
L'humidité de votre âme c'est ce qui vous reste de moi.
Je n'ai rien pu faire d'autre.
Je ne puis rien pour la mère dont va s'éteindre le fils
Sinon vous faire allumer, chandelles de l'espérance.
S'il n'en était pas ainsi, est-ce que vos connaîtriez,
Petits lits mal défendus, la paralysie des enfants.
Je suis coupé de mon œuvre,
Ce qui est fini est lointain et s'éloigne chaque jour.
Quand la source descend du mont comment revenir là-dessus?
Je ne sais pas plus vous parler qu'un potier ne parle à son pot,
Des deux il en est un de sourd, l'autre muet devant son œuvre
Et je vous vois avancer vers d'aveuglants précipices
Sans pouvoir vous les nommer,
Et je ne peux vous souffler comment il faudrait s'y prendre,
Il faut vous en tirer tout seuls comme des orphelins dans
        la neige.
Et je me dis chaque jour au delà d'un grand silence:
"Encore un qui fait de travers ce qu'il pourrait faire comme
        il faut,
Encore un qui fait un faux pas pour ne pas regarder où il doit.
Et cet autre qui se penche beaucoup trop sur son balcon,
Oubliant la pesanteur,
Et celui-là qui n'a pas vérifié son moteur,
Adieu avion, adieu homme!"
Je ne puis plus rien pour vous, hélas si je me répète
C'est à force d'en souffrir.
Je suis un souvenir qui descend, vous vivez dans un souvenir,
L'espoir qui gravit vos collines, vous vivez dans une espérance.
Secoué par les prières et les blasphèmes des hommes,
Je suis partout à la fois et ne peux pas me montrer,
Sans bouger je déambule et je vais de ciel en ciel,

Men, you whom I love well, I can do nothing for you in your
     misfortune,
I have only been able to give you your courage and your tears,
The warm assurances of God's existence.
The weeping of your soul is all you have left of me.
More than this I could not give.
I can do nothing for the mother whose son is about to die
Except to light you, tapers of faith.
If it were not so, would you recognize,
You little beds, so ill-defended, the child's paralysis?
I am cut off from the work of my hands.
Whatever is finished is far away and is farther away each day.
When the brook descends from the mountain, how shall it
     return?
I can no more speak to you than a potter can speak to his pot;
Of the two of them, one is deaf, the other dumb in the
     presence of his handiwork.
And I can see you advancing towards a blinding precipice
Without being able to tell you where it is,
And I cannot even hint to you how you should go about it;
You must find your way alone, like orphans in the snow.
And I say to myself each day, beyond the enormous silence:
"There goes another, making a mess of something he could do
     right,
There goes another, taking the wrong step, not looking where
     he is going.
And there is one who leans too far over his balcony railing,
Forgetting the law of gravity,
And there is one who hasn't checked his engine—
Farewell, airplane, and farewell, airman!
I can do nothing for you—I am sorry if I repeat myself—
It's because I feel all so strongly.
I am a memory that descends to earth, and you exist in it.
Shaken by the prayers and the blasphemies of men,
I am everywhere at once and may not advertise myself,
Without moving, I move, and I go from heaven to heaven,

Je suis l'errant en soi-même, et le grouillant solitaire,
Habitué des lointains, je suis très loin de moi-même,
Je m'égare au fond de moi comme un enfant dans les bois,
Je m'appelle, je me hale, je me tire vers mon centre.
Homme, si je t'ai créé c'est pour y voir un peu clair
Et pour vivre dans un corps moi qui n'ai mains ni visage.
Je veux te remercier de fair avec sérieux
Tout ce qui n'aura qu'un temps sur la Terre bien-aimée,
O mon enfant, mon chéri, ô courage de ton Dieu,
Mon fils qui t'en es allé courir le monde à ma place
A l'avant-garde de moi dans ton corps si vulnérable
Avec sa grande misère. Pas un petit coin de peau
Où ne puisse se former la profonde pourriture.
Chacun de vous sait faire un mort sans avoir eu besoin
    d'apprendre,
Un mort parfait qu'on peut tourner et retourner dans tous
    les sens,
Où il n'y a rien à redire.
Dieu vous survit, lui seul survit entouré par un grand massacre
D'hommes, de femmes et d'enfants
Même vivants, vous mourez un peu continuellement,
Arrangez-vous avec la vie, avec vos tremblantes amours.
Vous avez un cerveau, des doigts pour faire le monde à
    votre goût,
Vous avez des facilités pour faire vivre la raison
Et la folie en votre cage,
Vous avez tous les animaux qui forment la Création,
Vous pouvez courir et nager comme le chien et le poisson,
Avancer comme le tigre ou comme l'agneau de huit jours,
Vous pouvez vous donner la mort comme le renne, le scorpion,

I am wandering itself, and swarming solitude.
Familiar with the far-away, I keep my distance from myself
I lose my way within myself like a child in a forest;
I shout after myself, I shout halloo, and draw myself back to
my own center.
Man, if I created you, it was simply in order to get things
clear,
And so that I might live in a body, I who have neither hands
nor face.
I want to thank you for making a serious attempt
To do all that can be done in a little space on the well-loved
earth,
O my child, my darling, O courage that is from your God,
My son, you who have gone to walk the world in my place
Going before me in your so vulnerable,
So poorly provided body. There's not a shred of flesh
Where deep decay may not be lodged.
Each one of you can die without having ever learned how to,
And can make a perfect corpse that can be turned this way and
that,
One that is perfect in every way.
God outlives you, he alone outlives you in the midst of an aw-
ful massacre
Of men, women, and children.
Even when you are still alive, you are slowly and continually
dying;
Make your peace with life, and with your trembling loves.
You have a brain, fingers to fashion the world to the shape you
wish.
You have the gift of reason
And madness too,
You have all the animals of the Creation,
You can run and swim like the dogs and fishes,
Walk like a tiger or a week-old lamb,
You can give yourself the gift of death like the reindeer or the
scorpion,

Et moi je reste l'invisible, l'introuvable sur la Terre,
Ayez pitié de votre Dieu qui n'a pas su vous rendre heureux,
Petites parcelles de moi, ô palpitantes étincelles.
Je ne vous offre qu'un brasier où vous retrouverez du feu.

Nuit en moi, nuit au dehors,
Elles risquent leurs étoiles,
Les mêlant sans le savoir.
Et je fais force de rames
Entre ces nuits coutumières,
Puis je m'arrête et regarde.
Comme je me vois de loin!
Je ne suis qu'un frêle point
Qui bat vite et qui respire
Sur l'eau profonde entourante.
La nuit me tâte le corps
Et me dit de bonne prise.
Mais laquelle des deux nuits,
Du dehors ou du dedans?
L'ombre est une et circulante,
Le ciel, le sang ne font qu'un.
Depuis longtemps disparu,
Je discerne mon sillage
A grande peine étoilé.

And I remain invisible, the undiscoverable land.
Take pity on your God who did not know how to make you
    happy,
You small fractions of myself, O you shaking sparks
I offer you only a furnace where you can find your flame again.

                                     [J.K.]

NIGHT WITHIN ME

Night within me, night without,
Both imperiling their stars
That they ignorantly mingle.
And I row with steady strokes
In between these usual nights,
Then I pause and look:
What a long way off I seem!
I am but a tiny speck
That breathes and flutters rapidly
On the deep sea all around.
Night gropes on my body,
Finding me fair game.
But which night is it,
That without, or that within?
A single shadow encircles me,
Sky and blood are also one.
Though it has long since vanished,
I can discern my wake
Elaborately hung with stars.

                                     [J.K.]

LA PLUIE ET LES TYRANS

Je vois tomber la pluie
Dont les flaques font luire
Notre grave planète,
La pluie qui tombe nette
Comme du temps d'Homère
Et du temps de Villon
Sur l'enfant et sa mère
Et le dos des moutons,
La pluie qui se répète
Mais ne peut attendrir
La dureté de tête
Ni le cœur des tyrans
Ni les favoriser
D'un juste étonnement,
Une petite pluie
Qui tombe sur l'Europe
Mettant tous les vivants
Dans la même enveloppe
Malgré l'infanterie
Qui charge ses fusils
Et malgré les journaux
Qui nous font des signaux,
Une petite pluie
Qui mouille les drapeaux.

LE PETIT BOIS

J'étais un petit bois de France
Avec douze rouges furets,
Mais je n'ai jamais eu de chance
Ah! que m'est-il donc arrivé?

RAIN AND THE TYRANTS

I watch the falling rain
Whose plaques of water make our drab
Planet shine with light,
The rain that falls down pit-a-pat
As in the days of Homer
And the days of Villon,
Falling on the mother and the child
And on the sheep's woolly back,
The rain which is always rain
But cannot soften
The hard heads or the hard
Hearts of the tyrants,
Nor bless them with
A pardonable astonishment;
A gentle rain
Falling over Europe
Puts all the living
In the same envelope
In spite of the infantry
That loads its rifles
And in spite of the papers
That beckon to us,
A gentle rain
To wet the flags.

[J.K.]

FRANCE: THE LITTLE WOOD

I was once a little wood
With twelve red ferrets, O.
My luck was never any good,
O what has happened to me, O?

Je crains fort de n'être plus rien
Qu'un souvenir, une peinture
Ou le restant d'une aventure,
Un parfum, je ne sais pas bien.

Ne suis-je plus qu'en la mémoire
De quelle folle ou bien d'enfants,
Ils vous diraient mieux mon histoire
Que je ne fais en ce moment.

Mais où sont-ils donc sur la terre
Pour que vous les interrogiez,
Eux qui savent que je dis vrai
Et jamais je ne désespère.

Mon Dieu comme c'est difficile
D'être un petit bois disparu
Quand on avait tant de racines
Comment faire pour n'être plus?

HOMMAGE A LA VIE

C'est beau d'avoir élu
Domicile vivant
Et de loger le temps
Dans un cœur continu,
Et d'avoir vu ses mains
Se poser sur le monde
Comme sur une pomme
Dans un petit jardin,

I'm very much afraid my friend
I'll only be a memory, O,
A picture or a story's end,
A scent—that kind of thing, you know.

No one else now thinks of me
But silly old women and children, O;
They'll give you my sad history
Much better than I'm doing, O.

But where will you find them on earth
To ask them for to tell you, O?
For they alone know I speak true,
And never go despairing, O.

Dear Lord how hard it is to be
A little wood that's vanished, O.
With all those roots on every tree,
I don't know how I managed, O!

[J.K.]

HOMAGE TO LIFE

It is beautiful to have chosen
A living home
And stayed awhile,

And had its hands
Alight on the world,
As on an apple
In a little garden,

D'avoir aimé la terre,
La lune et le soleil,
Comme des familiers
Qui n'ont que leurs pareils,
Et d'avoir confié
Le monde à sa mémoire
Comme un clair cavalier
A sa monture noire,
D'avoir donné visage
A ces mots: femme, enfants,
Et servi de rivage
A d'errants continents,
Et d'avoir atteint l'âme
A petits coups de rame
Pour ne l'effaroucher
D'une brusque approchée.
C'est beau d'avoir connu
L'ombre sous le feuillage
Et d'avoir senti l'âge
Ramper sur le corps nu,
Accompagné la peine
Du sang noir dans nos veines
Et doré son silence
De l'étoile Patience,
Et d'avoir tous ces mots
Qui bougent dans la tête,
De choisir les moins beaux
Pour leur faire un peu fête,
D'avoir senti la vie
Hâtive et mal aimée,
De l'avoir enfermée
Dans cette poésie.

To have loved the earth,
The moon and the sun
Like old friends
Who have no equals,
And to have committed
The world to memory
Like a bright horseman
To his black steed,
To have given a face
To these words—woman, children,
And to have been a shore
On the wandering continents,
And to have come upon the soul
With tiny strokes of the oars,
For it is scared away
By a brusque approach.
It is beautiful to have known
The shade under the leaves,
And to have felt age
Creep over the naked body,
Accompanying the pain
Of black blood in ourselves,
And gilding its silence
With the star, Patience,
And to have all these words
Moving around in the head
To choose the least beautiful of them
And make a little feast,
To have felt life,
Hurried and ill loved,
To have ended it
In this poetry.

[K.R.]

PINS

O pins devant la mer,
Pourquoi donc insister
Par votre fixité
A demander réponse?
J'ignore les questions
De votre haut mutisme.
L'homme n'entend que lui,
Il en meurt comme vous.
Et nous n'eûmes jamais
Quelque tendre silence
Pour mélanger nos sables,
Vos branches et mes songes.
Mais je me laisse aller
A vous parler en vers,
Je suis plus fou que vous,
O camarades sourds,
O pins devant la mer,
O poseurs de questions
Confuses et touffues,
Je me mêle à votre ombre,
Humble zone d'entente,
Où se joignent nos âmes
Où je vais m'enfonçant,
Comme l'onde dans l'onde.

PLEIN CIEL

J'avais un cheval
Dans un champ de ciel
Et je m'enfonçais

PINES

O pine trees against the sea,
Why do you insist,
With such intensity,
Upon an answer?
I do not know the questions
Your lofty silence asks.
Man listens only to himself,
And dies of it, like you.
And never did we have
A tender space of silence
To bring our sands together,
Your branches and my dreams.
But here I am allowing myself
To speak to you in verse:
I'm as mad as you, or even more,
O friends who cannot hear,
O pines against the sea,
O askers of questions
That are dense as leaves.
I mingle with your shadow,
A humble no man's land
In which our souls may join
And I may lose myself
Like a wave within a wave.

[J.K.]

OPEN SKY

I once had a horse
In a field of sky
And I rode away

Dans le jour ardent.
Rien ne m'arrêtait
J'allais sans savoir,
C'était un navire
Plutôt qu'un cheval,
C'était un désir
Plutôt qu'un navire,
C'était un cheval
Comme on n'en voit pas,
Tête de coursier,
Robe de délire,
Un vent qui hennit
En se répandant.
Je montais toujours
Et faisais des signes:
"Suivez mon chemin,
Vous pouvez venir,
Mes meilleurs amis,
La route est sereine,
Le ciel est ouvert.
Mais qui parle ainsi?
Je me perds de vue
Dans cette altitude,
Me distinguez-vous,
Je suis celui qui
Parlait tout à l'heure,
Suis-je encor celui
Qui parle à présent,
Vous-mêmes, amis,
Etes-vous les mêmes?
L'un efface l'autre
Et change en montant."

In the burning day.
Nothing could stop
My dreamy gallop
—It was a ship
Instead of a horse,
It was desire
Instead of a ship,
It was a horse
Such as never was seen,
The head of a charger,
Its cloak was wild
With wind that neighed
And couldn't be held.
I went on soaring
And gave these signs:
—"Follow my lead,
You may follow me,
My finest friends,
For smooth is the way
And the sky is clear.
But who is it speaking?
I keep losing sight of myself
At this great altitude.
Can you make me out?
I am he
Who was speaking a moment ago,
But am I still
He who addresses you now,
And you, my friends, are
You still the same?
The one wipes out the other,
And, rising, changes."

[J.K.]

Ce bruit de la mer où nous sommes tous,
Il le connaît bien, l'arbre à chevelure,
Et le cheval noir y met l'encolure
Allongeant le cou comme pour l'eau douce,
Comme s'il voulait quitter cette dune,
Devenir au loin cheval fabuleux
Et se mélanger aux moutons d'écume,
A cette toison faite pour les yeux,
Etre enfin le fils de cette eau marine,
Brouter l'algue au fond de la profondeur.
Mais il faut savoir attendre au rivage,
Se promettre encore aux vagues du large,
Mettre son espoir dans la mort certaine,
Baisser de nouveau la tête dans l'herbe.

LE CLOS

Avec un mouvement
Qui vient de ses paupières,
Il fait un clos de pierres
Où il n'y avait rien,
Et puis, sans y songer,
Un second clos, de lierre,
Pour cacher le premier
Aux regards de la terre,
Et par-dessus le tout
Une petite brume
Où vous êtes aussi
O jamais importune,
Du poids de vos glycines
Devenues des fumées.

That sound, everywhere about us, of the sea—
the tree among its tresses has always heard it,
and the horse dips his black body in the sound
stretching his neck as if towards drinking water,
as if he were longing to leave the dunes and become
a mythic horse is the remotest distance,
joining the flock of foam-sheep—
fleeces made for vision alone—
to be indeed the son of these salt waters
and browse on algae in the deep fields.
But he must learn to wait, wait on the shore,
promising himself *someday* to the waves of the open sea,
putting his hope in certain death, lowering
his head again to the grass.

[D.L.]

THE ENCLOSURE

With a movement
That comes from his eyelids,
He makes a stone enclosure
Where once there was nothing.
And then, without thinking,
He makes another, of ivy
To conceal the first
From the eyes of earth,
And above it all
A little smoke
Where, O ever
Importunate, also abide,
Your heavy wistaria
Turned to smoke.

Et cela, il le fait
Avec rien qu'un petit
Battement de ses cils
Mais ne le dites pas
Il convient d'avancer
Avec indifférence
Et que rien ne se passe
Pour ceux qui ne sont pas
Dans le double secret
De tout ce faux silence.

Je vous rêve de loin, et, de près, c'est pareil,
Mais toujours vous restez précise, sans réplique,
Sous mes tranquilles yeux vous devenez musique,
Comme par le regard, je vous vois par l'oreille.

Vous savez être en moi comme devant mes yeux,
Tant vous avez le cœur offert, mélodieux,
Et je vous entends battre à mes tempes secrètes
Lorsque vous vous coulez en moi pour disparaître.

SONNET

A Pilar.

Pour ne pas être seul durant l'éternité,
Je cherche auprès de toi future compagnie
Pour quand, larmes sans yeux, nous jouerons à la vie
Et voudrons y loger notre fidélité.

And this he does
With only a little
Beat of his eyelids.
But never repeat it:
It's best to proceed
With an indifferent air.
And for those who are not
In the double secret
Of all this contrived silence,
Let nothing take place.

[J.K.]

I dream you into being, whether far away or near,
But always you remain distinct, and dumb,
Under my tranquil gazing you become
Music: as if it were an eye, I see you with my ear.

You can inhabit me as if you were before my eyes,
So wide-open and melodious is your heart,
And I hear you beating in my secret thought
When into my dream your disappearing presence flows.

[J.K.]

SONNET

                                        To Pilar

That we may not for ever be alone,
I seek in you my future company;
When, eyeless tears, we play at life that's gone,
Hoping to find a place for our fidelity,

Pour ne plus aspirer à l'hiver et l'été,
Ni mourir à nouveau de tant de nostalgie,
Il faut dès à présent labourer l'autre vie,
Y pousser nos grands bœufs enclins à s'arrêter,

Voir comment l'on pourrait remplacer les amis,
La France, le soleil, les enfants et les fruits,
Et se faire un beau jour d'une nuit coriace,

Regarder sans regard et toucher sans les doigts.
Se parler sans avoir de paroles ni voix,
Immobiles, changer un petit peu de place.

UN BRAQUE

Les poissons d'un si beau noir
Qu'ils remplacent tout espoir
Par plus de sérénité
Que n'en montre un bel été.
Noir intense, sa mémoire
Où tous les noirs viennent boire
Comme de fauves nocturnes
Tendant le cou vers l'obscur.
Et la vague de la nappe
Se soulève juste à point
Pour que toujours la rattrape
La blancheur qui la soutient.
Les objets sons sûrs d'eux-mêmes,
Rocs coupants devant la mer,
Et l'inconnu qui déferle
Les éclabousse de perles

That we may see the winter and the spring as done,
Not die a double death in our regretful memory,
We must begin to look towards that other sun,
And drive our cattle on, that pause continually.

What can we find to take the place of friends,
And France, and children, fruit and light,
And make a summer day of our persistent night?

How shall we touch, without our hands,
How speak, without words, and look, without faces;
And how, without moving, slightly shift our places?

[J.K.]

A PICTURE BY BRAQUE

Fish of so fine a black
That they replace all hope
By more serenity
Than a perfect summer.
Intensest black, a memory
Where all blacks come to drink
Like wild beasts at midnight
Stretching their necks towards obscurity.
And the vague cloth
Emerges just enough
To be constantly recaptured
By the whiteness underneath.
The objects are sure of themselves,
Rocks jutting into the sea,
And the unknown, mysteriously there,
Sprays them with pearls of light

Qui s'affermissent dans l'air.
Une forme ouvre la porte,
Se fige dans l'embrasure
Comme ferait une morte,
Mais elle se transfigure
En sagesse qui rassure
Et son calme grave et tendre
Dans sa langue nous exhorte,
Nous fait le signe d'attendre,
Puis elle ferme la porte.

Elle lève les yeux et la brise s'arrête,
Elle baisse les yeux, la campagne s'étend,
Elle tourne la tête une rose se prend
Au piège et la voilà qui tourne aussi la tête
Et jusqu'à l'horizon plus rien n'est comme avant.

Laissez-moi devenir olivier de Provence
Afin que familier de nouvelles nuances
Je donne encor des fruits prenant de moi conseil
Et mûris cette fois d'un visible soleil.

Un garçon non feuillu que l'on nomme Olivier
Verra comment grand-père administre ses branches
Et, prisonnier dorénavant de son seul pied,
Il huile son olive innombrable et se penche

Sur le monde ou sur lui d'un mouvement pareil
A travers quelque voile entre sombre et vermeil.

Suspended in the air.
A figure opens the door
And is transfixed in the opening
Like one struck dead;
But is then transformed.
Its wisdom reassures
And its grave and tender calm
Exhorts us in a language of its own,
Signals us to wait a moment more, then
Shuts the door.

[J.K.]

She lifts her eyes and the breeze is stilled,
Lowers her lids, and the landscape flows;
She turns her head, and a single rose
Is caught in the game, for it turns its head too,
And as far as the far horizon, nothing is the same again.

[J.K.]

Let me become an olive tree of Provence
so that, familiar with new subtleties,
I may give fruit yet, taking counsel with myself,
to ripen, this time, in a visible sun.

A boy not yet in leaf whom one calls Oliver
will see in what fashion grandfather orders his branches
and, from now on prisoner of his one foot,
oils his innumerable olives, and leans

over the world or over him with the same movement
across some veil between shadow and crimson.

[D.L.]

STORIES

translated by Enid McLeod

THE CREATION OF THE ANIMALS

The animals fell from the heavens one by one without hurting themselves. Most of them were already completed, but some had still to wait a little before they got all their appurtenances.

"It seems I'm to have a trunk," said the elephant, who had newly arrived. "It'll start from my forehead and hang down almost to the ground."

"That's a lot for a nose," said the fox.

"It's exactly what I need," retorted the elephant.

He had hardly finished his sentence when the trunk arrived from the furthest spaces of the heavens, to take the place which it was henceforth to occupy in all elephants.

"Ought I to bark?" wondered the dog, whose voice was already developed. "No, I'll keep silent, that's the correct thing."

The only thing the horse lacked was his ears, but he was so busy trying to get rid of his shadow as he galloped that he was unaware of the fact. The ears caught up with him when he was going full tilt and they have still not recovered from their astonishment, and never stop swiveling in all directions.

"Rumor has it," said the horse, "that no one will ever gallop faster than I. I don't yet know very well what that means, but I guess I am going to be very proud of it."

Suddenly, all of them felt very uncomfortable. The donkey had just brayed. He had spewed out the noise in front of everyone and seemed pleased about it.

The Creator went from one animal to another, adding this and that, and making trifling adjustments. He had just given his stripes to the zebra, who was thrilled with them and was showing them to everyone.

"There's no reason to be so proud of them," said the donkey. "All those stripes are utterly useless."

"That may be, but at least I'm not obliged to bray to make sure I'm not forgotten."

The hippopotamus, the rhinoceros, the camel, and the dromedary lived in a group. The toad, the owl, and the marabou felt drawn to them and followed them everywhere, no one quite knew why. It was only discovered much later that it was for aesthetic reasons, and they were then told so. They answered that they were still only roughly outlined, and that one would have to see when the Creator had had time to consider the question.

The bear wondered whether he was really finished, but said nothing about this to anyone. He was looking all over the place for a kind of wild jam. He found it and called it honey.

The viper said that his paws would soon be delivered to him, that he was in fact expecting them from one moment to the next. "When I'm able to carry my poison at top speed from one end of the earth to the other, then you'll see!"

"Hold your tongue!" said the great voice from behind the clouds. "In the first place, who told you you were going to have paws?"

"Logic!" boldly answered one of the serpents.

"Very well then, I will take your poison away from you and you shall be called grass snakes. That will be your punishment."

And so it still is.

A serpent of another type, which had kept silent, retained his poison. The grass snake appealed against the divine decision, affirming that if he had protested it was because he did not yet quite know how to use the ideas which he had in his head.

"Fiddlesticks!" was all that the voice behind the clouds replied.

There was certainly no time to get bored. Something unexpected happened every minute.

"Just look," said a bird, "at that object taller than an elephant. The minute the wind blows, it waves all those hundreds of little things tied on to its branches."

"That," said the voice from behind the clouds, "is what I call a tree. It's yours to make use of."

"By doing what?" asked the monkey. The voice did not reply, but a strong, invisible forefinger pushed a cow into the shade of the tree, where she lay down. And immediately other beasts began to imitate her. As it was a hot day, everyone understood.

There were also flowers everywhere. The animals looked at them suspiciously. They could not see what they were for.

"They aren't any use but they're pretty," said the voice.

Pretty. No one quite knew what that meant. By dint of believing in the word, they ended by understanding.

All of a sudden, each one found himself face to face with an animal which was the very image of himself. Since each thought he was the only one of his kind, they began by resenting these others. Full of mistrust, they fled, but observed each other from a distance.

"Unite with one another!" said the voice from behind the clouds. "Increase and multiply!"

"I don't see the connection," said someone who thought himself very intelligent.

"Circle round each other until you understand."

Like a trail of gunpowder, the rumor began to spread that there were males and females and that the different sexes took much pleasure in each other's company.

They began to have little ones. The females were delighted at this, but the males were not sure what to think of those tiny replicas, the need for which was not apparent.

"Is it true that we are going to eat each other? For my part, I really don't know how I should set about it," said the wolf to the lamb, in a voice dripping with false modesty, gazing meanwhile at the little woolly one with a benevolence which came much more from his stomach than his heart.

"I really wonder what all this is leading up to," said the bear. "But we mustn't be in a hurry to come to a conclusion."

One fine day, the animals gathered round one of their number—it was a dog—who had been shamming dead since the day before. No matter how much they touched or nibbled or bit him, he did not budge. And the bitch cried: "Let him alone, can't you! You know very well he never liked getting up early."

The next day the dog, not content with not moving, began to smell bad—which was indeed movement of a kind, in the sense of smell at least. The bitch maintained that there were others, like the lion, who smelt much stronger, and that no one minded that. But the voice from behind the clouds (they called him that even when the weather was fine) cried, "Don't bother with this dog. He's no longer good for anything. That is what I call a corpse."

"Surely you don't cast away like that people who have nothing to reproach themselves with?" wailed the bitch. "Think of it, an animal who, barely two days ago, enjoyed universal esteem, now lies decomposing in stench, and the only consolation offered is to tell us not to bother about him any more."

"Increase and multiply," retorted the voice from behind the clouds.

"No desire to!" replied the animals in chorus.

"The desire will come!" said the voice.

And they began to multiply again, but this time not without melancholy.

For some time past there had been a great deal of talk about a being to come, who would be extremely handy with his front paws and whose head would be full of resource. "We've been talking about him for such ages," said the bear, "that I begin to think he'll never arrive."

The man, in the flower of his youth, was deposited in the midst of the assembly of beasts, and at once began to look about him as if he had always had eyes.

Without even taking the trouble to greet those present, he made all sorts of movements with his arms and hands. He did standing jumps, ran, marched backward without turning round, lay down, knelt, hopped on one foot, went on all fours, leapt to his feet with a bound, lunged like a fencer, whistled, and spat on his hands.

"I eat without being hungry," he said, "drink without being thirsty, weep without sorrow, and sleep without wanting to." And he was so pleased with himself that he laughed and spun round on his heels.

The lion was the first to recover his composure. "Poor devil," he said, "he's cunning and skillful, but he can hardly last more than a few days. And it will be child's play for the winter cold to pierce that defenseless skin with its arrows of frost."

They were astonished that the Creator, who was better inspired as a rule, had taken the trouble to make a being so weak and so poorly supplied with hair. Out of mockery an orangutan tore out a good handful of his own and offered it to him. The man took the hair, blew on it, and again burst out laughing. He picked up stones and hurled them a great distance, not wounding anyone but just missing all of them; then, with his voice and gestures, he imitated, one after another, and very well too, the cat, the dog, the horse, the tiger, the lion, the elephant, and finally the orangutan.

Then he whistled for his female, who ran up at a gentle trot, caressed her, kissed her, and lay with her, after which they both went to sleep and snored under the noses of all the animals.

The next day he improvised a little country workshop and set to work to fashion an ax and a knife of flint. He covered himself with feathers and fur and put some of them on his wife's back also. He collected some twigs and then some logs, rubbed two stones against each other, and made a big fire crowned with smoke. Then he applauded himself with obvious pleasure, swore and sang at the top of his voice.

He was the first tenor, the first fire maker, the first furrier, the first juggler, the first stonecutter, the first man to have no shame, the first blasphemer.

He killed a viper on the pretext that it was poisonous, and

a grass snake because it wasn't. He dealt with death as easily as he dealt with logic and sentimental songs, so much so that the beasts, taken aback, lost the power of speech, though this aphasia was not complete. They kept, as we know, the right to roar, trumpet, bark, whinny, and bray, a right which, even to this day, they do not deny themselves.

THE CHILD OF THE OPEN SEA

How had that floating street been created? What sailors, with the aid of what architects, had built it in mid-Atlantic, on the surface of the sea, over a gulf thousands of fathoms deep? That long street with its red brick houses, so faded that they were turning French gray, those roofs of slate and tile, those unchanging, humble shops? And that richly perforated belfry? And this place which had nothing but sea water in it, though no doubt it wanted to be a garden, with enclosing walls set with broken bottle glass, over which a fish would sometimes leap?

How did it remain standing without even being tossed by the waves?

And that solitary twelve-year-old child who walked in her sabots with a firm step down the liquid street as though she were walking on dry land? How did it come about?

We shall relate all these things as we get to know and understand them. And if anything remains obscure it will not be our fault.

Whenever a ship approached, even before it could be seen on the horizon, a great drowsiness took possession of the child, and the village disappeared completely beneath the waves. And thus it was that no sailor had ever seen the village, even at the end of a telescope, or even suspected its existence.

The child thought she was the only little girl in the world. Did she even know she was a little girl? She was not very pretty, because of her rather wide-spaced teeth, and her rather too tip-tilted nose, but she had a very white skin with a few speckles—I mean freckles. And her small person, dominated by gray eyes that were shy but very luminous, sent through your body, right into your soul, a great surprise which hailed from the night of time.

Sometimes in the street, the only one in that little town, the child would look to right and left as if she were expecting a friendly sign from someone, a slight wave of the hand or a nod of the head. This was merely an impression she gave without knowing it, since no person or thing could come to that lost village that was always ready to vanish.

How did she live? By fishing? We don't think so. She found food in the kitchen cupboard and larder, and even meat every two or three days. There were also potatoes for her and a few other vegetables, and eggs from time to time.

Provisions appeared spontaneously in the cupboards. And when the child took jam from a pot, it remained as intact as before, as if things had been thus one day and had to stay the same for ever.

In the mornings, half a pound of fresh bread, wrapped in paper, was waiting for the child on the marble counter of the bakery, behind which she had never seen anyone, not even a hand or a finger pushing the bread towards her.

She was always up early, and she would push up the metal screens of the shops (one labeled "Bar," and others "Blacksmith," "Modern Bakery," or "Haberdasher"), open the shutters of all the houses, carefully fastening them back because of the sea wind, and, according to the weather, leaving the windows closed or not. She would light a fire in a few kitchens so that smoke should rise from three or four roofs. An hour before sunset she began, very simply, to close the shutters and to lower the corrugated metal screens.

The child accomplished these tasks, moved by some instinct,

some daily inspiration which drove her to look after everything. In the summer months, she would hang a rug over a window sill, or some linen to dry, as though the village must at all costs look inhabited and as lifelike as possible. And the whole year round she had to take care of the town-hall flag, which was so exposed.

At night she used candles, or sewed by the light of a lamp. There was electricity, too, in several houses in the town, and the child turned the switches easily and gracefully.

On one occasion she put a black crepe bow on the knocker of a door. She thought it looked nice. It remained there for two days, after which she hid it.

Another time she started beating a drum, the village drum, as though she were going to announce some news. And she had a violent longing to shout something that might have been heard from one end of the sea to the other; but her throat contracted and no sound came out. She made such a stern effort that her face and neck became almost black with it, like those of drowned people. Then she had to put the drum back in its usual place, in the left-hand corner at the far end of the big hall of the town hall.

The child reached the belfry by a spiral staircase whose steps were worn by thousands of unseen feet. The belfry which, the child thought, must certainly have five hundred steps (it had ninety-two) showed as much sky as it could between its yellow bricks. And she had to satisfy the weight-driven clock by winding it up with the crank handle, so that it should sound the hours exactly, day and night.

The crypt, the altars, the stone saints giving silent orders, all those faintly whispering chairs which waited, in straight rows, for people of all ages, those altars whose gold had aged and hoped to age still more—all that attracted and repelled the child, who never entered that tall house, contenting herself, when she had nothing else to do, with sometimes half opening the padded door and darting a rapid glance at the interior, holding her breath as she did so.

In a trunk in her room there were family papers and some postcards from Dakar, Rio de Janeiro, and Hong Kong signed Charles or C. Lievens, and addressed to Steenvoorde (Nord). The child of the open sea had no idea what those far countries and this Charles and this Steenvoorde were.

She also kept an album of photographs in a cupboard. One of them showed a child who looked very like the little girl of the Ocean, who would often gaze at it humbly; it was always this picture which seemed to her to be right, to ring true; she was holding a hoop in her hand. The child had looked for one like it in all the houses of the village. And one day she thought she had found one; it was the iron hoop of a barrel; but hardly had she begun to run down the marine street with it than the hoop bowled out to sea.

In another photograph the little girl was seen between a man dressed in sailor's clothes and a bony woman in her Sunday best. The child of the open sea, who had never seen either man or woman, wondered for a long time what those people wanted, even thinking about it in the dead of night, when lucidity sometimes strikes you suddenly with the violence of a thunderbolt.

Every morning she went to the village school, with a big satchel containing notebooks, a grammar, an arithmetic, a history of France, and a geography. She also had, written by Gaston Bonnier, member of the *Institut* and professor at the *Sorbonne,* and Georges de Layens, laureate of the *Académie des Sciences,* a little field guide which listed the most common plants, as well as useful and harmful plants, with eight hundred and ninety-six illustrations.

She read in the preface: "During the whole of the summer, there is nothing easier than to get hold of a great number of field and forest flowers."

And how were history, geography, countries, great men, mountains, rivers, and frontiers to be explained to someone who has nothing but the empty street of a little town in the most solitary part of the Ocean? She did not even know that she was on the Ocean, the very one she saw on the maps, although the idea did cross her mind one day, for a second. But she had driven it away as mad and dangerous.

Now and then, she would listen with complete obedience, write a few words, listen again and begin writing again, as though at the dictation of an invisible mistress. Then the child would open a grammar and remain for a long time, holding her breath and bending over page 60 and exercise CLXVIII, of which she was particularly fond. In it the grammar seemed to be speaking entirely for the benefit of the little girl of the open sea:

— are you? — are you thinking? — do you speak? — do you want? — should one apply to? — is happening? — is being accused? — are you capable? — are you guilty? — is the matter? — do you like this present? — are you complaining?
(Replace the dashes by the appropriate interrogative pronoun, with or without preposition.)

Sometimes the child felt a very persistent longing to write certain phrases, and did so with a great deal of concentration. Here are some of them, among many others:

Let's share this, shall we?
Listen to me carefully. Sit down and don't move, I beg you!
If I only had a little snow from the high mountains, the day would pass more quickly.
Foam, foam all round me, won't you at last turn into something solid?
To play a round game you have to be at least three.
There were two headless shadows walking away along the dusty road.
The night, the day, the day, the night, the clouds and the flying fish.
I thought I heard a noise, but it was the noise of the sea.

Or else she wrote a letter in which she gave news of her little town and herself. It wasn't addressed to anyone and she put no kisses for anyone at the end of it, and on the envelope there was no name. And when the letter was finished she threw it into the sea, not to get rid of it but because it had to be that way, and perhaps in the manner of navigators in distress, who consign their last message to the waves in a despairing bottle.

Time never passed in the floating town: the child was always twelve. And it was in vain that she swelled out her little chest before the glass-fronted cupboard of her room. One day, tired of looking, with her plaits and her very bare forehead, like the photo she kept in her album, she got cross with herself and her picture and scattered her locks roughly over her shoulders, hoping that this would give her age a jolt. Perhaps it would even affect the sea all round her, and she would see coming out of it great goats, with foaming beards, who would draw near to look at her.

But the Ocean remained empty and she received no other visits than those of the shooting stars.

Another day destiny seemed to forget itself for a moment, as though there were a sudden crack in its will. A real little cargo boat, all smoking, as obstinate as a bulldog and riding easily although it was not heavily loaded (a beautiful red band gleamed in the sun under the water line)—a cargo boat passed down the marine street of the village, without the houses disappearing beneath the waves nor the little girl's getting overcome with sleep.

It was just midday. The cargo boat sounded its siren, but this voice did not mingle with the voice of the belfry. Each kept its independence. The child, hearing for the first time a noise which came to her from men, rushed to the window and shouted with all her might:

"Help!"

And she flung her schoolgirl's pinafore in the direction of the ship.

The helmsman did not even turn his head. And a sailor, who was puffing smoke from his mouth, passed along the deck as if nothing had happened. The others went on washing their clothes, while on each side of the ship's bow dolphins separated to make room for the cargo boat, which was in a hurry.

The little girl descended very quickly into the street, lay down on the track of the ship, and embraced its wake for such a long time that, when she got up, nothing remained of it but a stretch of sea with no memory, quite intact. On returning to the house, the child was dumbfounded at having shouted: "Help!" Only then did she understand the profound meaning of this word. And this meaning terrified her. Could men not hear her voice? Or were those sailors deaf and blind? Or more cruel than the depths of the sea?

Then a wave, which had always remained at some distance from the village, clearly not wishing to intrude, came to look for her. It was a huge wave, which spread much further than the others on each side of itself. In its crest it had what looked exactly like two eyes, made of foam. You would have supposed it understood certain things and did not approve of them all. Although it furled and unfurled itself hundreds of times a day, it never forgot to equip itself with those two well-formed eyes, in the same place. Sometimes, when something interested it, you would catch it lingering for nearly a minute, with its crest in the air, forgetting its wave nature and that it had to begin again every seven seconds.

For a long time this wave had been wanting to do something for the child, but it did not know what. It saw the cargo boat disappearing and understood the anguish of the little girl who remained behind. Not being able to bear it any longer, it carried her a little distance away, without saying a word, as though leading her by the hand.

After having knelt before her, wave-fashion, and with the greatest respect, it tucked her under itself and kept her for a very long moment, trying to confiscate her with the collaboration of death. And the little girl stopped breathing to help the wave in this serious plan.

Failing to achieve its object, it flung her into the air until the child was no bigger than a sea swallow, catching her again and again like a ball as she fell back among the foam flakes big as ostrich eggs.

Finally, seeing that nothing was of any avail, that it could not succeed in giving her death, the wave took the child back to her home, with an immense murmur of tears and excuses.

And the little girl, who had not received a scratch, had to begin opening and closing shutters again without hope, and disappearing momentarily under the sea the moment the mast of a ship showed on the horizon.

Sailors who dream upon the high seas, with your elbows propped on the handrail, be fearful lest you dwell too long in the darkness of the night on a beloved face. For if you do, you risk giving birth, in places that are essentially deserted, to a being gifted with every human sensibility, who can neither live nor die nor love, and yet suffers as though he lived and loved and was always on the point of death, a being infinitely disinherited in the watery solitudes, like that child of the Ocean, born one day in the mind of Charles Lievens, of Steenvoorde, deck hand of the four-master *Fearless,* who had lost his twelve-year-old daughter during one of his voyages, and one night, at a place 55 degrees latitude North and 35 degrees longitude West, thought of her for a long time, with terrible intensity, to the great misfortune of that child.

THE WIFE REFOUND

Chemin was a little man with a short black beard, who fell asleep every evening well pleased with himself because he had just polished his shoes so carefully that he felt he could go anywhere at all next day without injuring his reputation.

He was very fond of his wife, who was fifteen years younger than himself. In his eyes she had only one fault, but it was one which caused him a great deal of pain: she could not keep to herself certain inopportune reflections, which would burst from her like a sudden splutter. She would then laugh to show how little importance she attached to these remarks; but has a laugh ever been able to efface anything?

For all that, he had lived a happy enough life until one summer day when she said to him: "Paul, your nose is getting bigger as you get older." As always when he had taken something too much to heart, he said nothing in reply; but the next day, without a word of warning, he left for England on a fishing boat, in order to give his wife a lesson which, as it turned out, he had to learn himself, since he was shipwrecked.

On his arrival in the Beyond, he was urged to express a wish, whereupon he quickly said: "I would like to have a small nose. I don't care about anything else." They showed him various models and he chose one that was small, but as expressive as an eye.

"Don't choose one that's too beautiful," said the official in charge of the noses, a former hatter who was an expert at knowing when things suited people or not.

"Oh, this one'll do very well."

From time to time Paul Chemin passed his hand over it; how nice it felt to the touch! It was a real marvel of a nose. Unfortunately it attracted attention in the gray street of heaven, like a hat of far too light a color on a dull day.

The next day he went back to the man with a thousand noses. "You're right," he said, "I'd like something simpler."

"I didn't want to insist when you chose it. We don't force anyone here. But I see what you ought to have." They went and fetched a nose exactly like Chemin's old one before it began to grow bigger. "With this nose," said the purveyor, "you'll have no difficulties."

"And now," said Chemin to himself as he left, "I simply must show myself like this to my wife."

The poor wretch thought he would be able to find her in the Beyond, a common delusion among the newly arrived dead. At the moment of death they had all received such a blow on the memory that they imagined they could still associate with those they had just left. And it was necessary to announce to them, taking the greatest care to put it kindly, that so-and-so was still living, and so was someone else, and that in fact, of all their relations and friends, they were almost the only ones to be dead.

Chemin looked about him. There was not a single angel's feather to be seen in this part of heaven. Nor was there any suggestion of God and the Saints either. A few people maintained that they had existed once upon a time, but no one could remember them. Was it merely a divine lull? Was God preparing some great offensive in secret? It began to seem doubtful, although there still remained up there traces of a supernatural power from which the dead benefited. Thus, you could choose your own climate, and wherever you went your climate made a point of following you. That did not at all interfere with the tastes of your neighbors. You could lie stretched on the grass and feel perfectly warm, while the man your elbow was touching was traveling in a sleigh in the middle of the night through a dense Siberian snowstorm.

There were other advantages which revealed themselves little by little to those concerned. One day Chemin noticed that a bit of his past was being projected in front of him as though on a screen. All you had to do, in order to see some part of your former existence, was to think about it rather intently. So that was the cinema of memory, which he had heard his companions talking about!

That day Chemin's screen was showing the shipwreck in which he had come by his death. The picture was so distinct and convincing that he asked a few comrades to come and see it. This was a courtesy which the leisured people of the Beyond often showed one another, one of the few distractions in that world where you were not obliged to work to earn your living.

A shipwreck is always an upsetting thing to see, but when you are the hero of it! When you see yourself struggling in the tempest! Previously he had wondered just how his death had occurred. Now he saw it in all its details. He had actually died in saving a cabin boy on that wretched fishing boat. The spectators near him began to applaud. They congratulated him on his heroic death. Ah yes, there was no doubt his wife had not known how to appreciate him properly.

In this way did memory give up its secrets. You could feel it functioning half-consciously. Many things you thought you had completely forgotten projected themselves as freshly and vividly as life itself. But you invited your friends only to important viewings which you had inspected in advance. You had to be rather cautious: some private event would appear when you least expected it, and it was better, as they say, to wash one's dirty linen at home. Besides, in everyone's life there are repetitions and many periods when time drags, and to be continually obliged to press the middle of your forehead with your forefinger, to make the memory accelerator work, created a bad impression, even among your best friends.

Chemin decided to watch the projections by himself, not caring to be consoled, if need arose. At first, he avoided seeing his wife again, as he still felt vexed with her. As soon as she appeared, he pressed the middle of his forehead, preferring to watch himself surrounded by his pupils, for instance, when he was giving his lessons, or playing tennis with his colleagues at the primary school. But since it was the only question which really interested him, he decided one day to devote himself to discovering what part his wife had really played in his life.

There was no doubt she was very photogenic. Never had he seen her look so pretty. Just plump enough for someone as lean and dry as he, and fresh as a daisy even first thing in the morning. Most women take such a long time to pull themselves together on emerging from sleep, but she always woke up immediately.

It was true they did not even have a charwoman. He realized it now. It was quite time he began to pity his wife, who every day had to wash, iron, brush, heat, cook, and keep things cool . . . almost all the verbs in the dictionary. And how full of intelligent tenderness was the look she gave him the day when he put on his new suit, the latest one, which must have gotten so wet during the shipwreck.

The closeups, as if on purpose, always emphasized some particularly nice thing which his wife had done for him, as for instance when she used to give him the choicest bit, keeping the bone and fat for herself, or when she paid the gas bill with the money he gave her for her clothes.

Ah, why then had he left home? And to get shipwrecked! Serve him right, idiot that he was! And now he had to be satisfied with the humble life of a dead person.

Sometimes, in spite of himself, Chemin loitered in the Square of the Newcomers in the hope of seeing his wife arrive there. But all of a sudden he would think: "No, no, no, I can't wish for the death of the being I love best in the world"; and he would rush away as fast as his legs could carry him.

In every part of the Beyond one was painfully aware of the silence. Never a sound, except in one small round place in the sky. This was the Circus of Perfect Echoes, where one could very distinctly hear, several centuries later, cries which rose from the Earth: cries of crowds gathered for some great event, cries of battle, cries of children during their playtime.

At that time there was a lot of talk about the echoes of the battle of Salamis. After being on their way for two millennia, they were just about to reach the Circus of the Echoes, at least if one believed the calculations of the astronomers and sound engineers. The Athenian and Persian generals were urging everyone not to go too far away.

And, in fact, thousands of shouts did suddenly reverberate through the Circus, making the different episodes astonishingly real once again. And although they had sworn not to get angry, the great contending leaders could not prevent themselves from exchanging abuse, under the reproving glances of Hellenists from all periods.

It annoyed Chemin a great deal to have to live in an anachronistic present in this way, and he did not conceal his ill humor. "All those loud-mouthed brutes of two thousand years ago don't mean a thing to me," he said to one of his former colleagues, whom he had found again. "I never did care for Greek history and here are the generals trying to force me to live it. It's my wife's voice I want to hear."

If he could only have seen her!

"Chemin, old boy, stop thinking of your wife," an inner voice said to him. "You mustn't expect too much of her. You've been a schoolmaster; that ought to have taught you to be reasonable."

Now one day he found himself in a public square where there were perhaps a hundred thousand telescopes. It was a most impressive sight. Slightly surprised that so many of the dead should be interested in astronomy, he mingled with the crowd. The square was full of observers of all ages. And nothing amused the children of the Beyond so much as to see the children of Earth playing hopscotch at the other end of those exquisitely perfected spyglasses.

A father would be on the lookout for his daughter, a girl searching for her lover, and another girl for her school friend. They were all waiting, standing with their instruments at the exit of some building—a five-storeyed house, factory, workshop, or country house; and all of them had their eyes fixed on that old Earth where something was happening, because in the Beyond, now that they no longer feared death, it seemed as though nothing important ever occurred any more. Audacity, patience, imagination, will, even love itself, none of them had a meaning any more. Each man appeared to the other merely as a problem that had been settled, whereas in the world there was always an element of the unknown right up to the last breath.

Chemin, who had once been a sergeant, asked to see the Earth.

"Nothing but the Earth?" The man had a slightly ironical look that you often find in keepers of telescopes.

"I'd like to see again someone I left down there."

"Your wife, perhaps," said the man, with the same smile.

"That isn't forbidden, as far as I know . . ."

"Well, I'm not giving you orders, but I don't advise it. There's always something we don't much like in the attitude of those we've left; it may be that they're really taking too much care not to get run over when they're crossing the road, or else that they're taking a second helping of a dish we used to like particularly."

"I'd prefer to be unhappy if I must—it'll give me something to think about."

"There's no need to get angry."

He pointed the apparatus in a certain direction and turned several crank handles.

"What part of Paris do you want to see?"

"The rue des Canettes, if it's possible," said Chemin, mollified.

"It's always possible here, when people ask things politely." Oh, there it was, life flowing along, the real life of the living! Men and women coming and going on their well-tried legs. What a seething crowd in the rue des Canettes! And all those housewives and street barrows! He looked for his wife at the door of No. 27. It was nine o'clock down there, it wouldn't be long before she went out to do the shopping.

Suddenly he saw her. She was wearing a black dress, completely black, without the least little ornament.

"It's because of me! She must have seen the list of the drowned in the papers," thought Chemin proudly, gripping his telescope tightly. "And to think I left home without even saying *au revoir* to her!"

He couldn't look at her enough. How fresh and pretty she was! And living so easily. How bright everything was on the

Earth! And to think there were people who committed suicide!

Everything on the planet seemed to him worthy of affection: the merest fragment of wood deserved to be considered with attention, the tiniest insect merited your interest, and the smallest pebble was important enough to have some of its dirt brushed off.

At first, Chemin always needed the help of the keeper to find Paris. Now he could easily have discovered it for himself, except that it was raining a lot over France. For several days visibility was zero.

"And doesn't it ever rain here?" the former teacher asked the keeper.

"You can see it doesn't."

"Doesn't that get a bit monotonous in the long run?"

"My job is to show the landscape and not to criticize anyone or anything."

To pass the time, Chemin and some of his colleagues went over the geography of the countries which were enjoying fine weather. "That's the Pacific," he said one day. "Look!"

"The Pacific, that! I know the Pacific, I do. I was a teacher at Tonkin. What you're pointing to there is the Atlantic. I can easily tell that from the length of the waves."

But the keeper proved to them that they were both wrong, by showing them Odessa.

At other times they would quarrel over the name of some town or other. "I tell you it's a subprefecture. Wait a second, the name's on the tip of my tongue."

"Can one keep the apparatus a long time?"

"As long as you like," said the keeper.

Sometimes, tiring of geography and discussions in front of the telescope, the two teachers caught themselves making plans for the future, or trying to find some former colleague among the daily throng of new arrivals. Up there, hunting for people you knew was the main distraction. You would find yourself on the lookout even for people who had not much interested you, and they ended by becoming indispensable to you. Besides, any excuse was good enough for striking up a friendship.

People of the same profession tended to get together, as did also victims of the same disease: typhoid fever, cancer, etc. As a result of a rumor that Chemin had taken his own life, it was suggested to him that he should join the Brotherhood of Suicides. It was this which decided him, for the sake of truth, to become a member of the Society for Shipwrecked Parisians, whose badge he wore in order to keep recruiters from other associations at a distance.

On more than one occasion, when he was watching his past again in the films shown by his memory, Chemin wished he could touch up his former life, modifying this or that. Why had he been satisfied with being a teacher? Ought he not to have provided his wife with a more agreeable life? Aimed higher, in fact? He would ask himself this when, here and there, he met some of the illustrious dead: Richelieu, Galileo or Christopher Columbus, the first Rothschilds, Monsieur Boucicaut, and the five or six Homers. All these personages were "someone" for eternity, and were followed by a great number of faithful. Whenever the great man halted, they stopped too, taking up positions around him or, as they said, making their arrangements for the night. For many of them, to attach themselves to a defunct notability, or even to a member of his suite, provided a justification for their "existence." That was why one saw shades dogging the footsteps of Ravaillac who, with the subtle smile of a connoisseur, was still following Henri IV, not from any evil intention, certainly, but merely out of concern for historical truth.

At last the weather over France turned fine once more, and Chemin was able to see his wife again, just when she was leaving the baker's, a few million leagues away. And now there she was choosing tomatoes from a little barrow.

"Why doesn't she take that one on the left, it's much the finest. There, on the left, I tell you! Oh dear, how far away she is!" he thought bitterly. "And to think I can't even give her a word of advice!"

Now that he could only see her at the end of this posthumous telescope, he realized that, throughout his life, he had never talked to his wife about the only thing that mattered: what she meant or could mean to him, and what he would have liked to mean to her. He had been satisfied that his relations with Elise should be those of a mere associate in the same business: the business of everyday life.

One day he discovered her at the moment when she was going into the florist's. Then, with her bunch of flowers in her hand, she caught a bus. After that she disappeared from view on the rear platform of the bus. But finally he saw her get down at Père-Lachaise cemetery to go and put flowers on her husband's grave. "It's really very good of you to do that, Elise." And addressing a keeper he said: "Why ever are there so many people at Père-Lachaise today?"

"It's All Souls' Day."

"Oh!" said Chemin, disappointed, "I'd much rather they didn't think of us in the lump."

"You should take good things as they come," said the keeper, "and not find fault with your treats."

Sometimes for hours together he would train his telescope on her front door. How well he knew that doorstep and the façade of No. 27! Never had he looked at them so much before. But nothing at the end of the glass made any sound, neither factories, cars, or conversation, the children at their play, the birds in their enjoyment, nor the great cascade on the racecourse at Longchamp.

"It's really very unfortunate, all that fine weather down there," said the keeper of the telescope to him one day, noticing how unhappy he looked at the end of the glass. "You're not supposed to come here to distress yourself. Why don't you take a rest? Hang it all, look about you!"

"I shall have plenty of time to take an interest in things here. I want to see my wife again."

"Well, then, if you won't be reasonable, I'm very sorry to say that I can't let you go on looking through my apparatus."

Chemin took himself off, determined that next day he would go to a different keeper.

When he picked out his wife again, she was on her balcony. In her hand she was holding the notebook in which she used to put down her thoughts, and which hitherto she had always carefully hidden from him. Down there it was a day in mid-May. The sunlight fell gaily and caressingly on the page, and over his widow's shoulder Chemin read without difficulty:

July 20th. Paul looked very worried today. He has a lofty mind. He often soars to regions where it's difficult for me to reach him.

"But that's not in the least true," thought Chemin, "I never soared at all."

July 25th. He was sulky with me again today. It's obvious I don't do things properly.

"But you did things very well indeed, my poor child. It was I who didn't understand you."

August 3rd. Oh dear, oh dear, why did he leave for England one fine day without even saying au revoir to me?

August 5th. Paul, I forgive you. I didn't know how to live up to you.

"But you're on the wrong tack," cried, or rather murmured, Chemin with all his might into his telescope (in the Beyond everyone was voiceless), "I never loved anyone but you."

August 6th. The concierge and some neighbors have been up to show me the evening paper. Paul has been ship-wrecked!!!

August 7th. On the list of those who have been lost, there is a Ginette Lucien. Perhaps it was with her that my poor Paul . . .

THE WIFE REFOUND • 119

"But it's not true. Ah, who will undeceive her? How sad it is to be so far apart! But I can see you, Elise, I can see you. How pretty she is in her half-mourning! It was an awfully good idea to leave off that veil, she wore it only too long. And now, my darling, you must live, go where you like, eat, look, and, if it amuses you, make love!"

A few days elapsed, about what on earth we should call a week.

A telescope keeper for whom Chemin had developed a friendship told him that one of their comrades in death had succeeded in returning to Earth. This keeper seemed to be trustworthy enough, since for a long time in the Beyond he had worn on his sleeve and his chest more stripes and badges than a sergeant major in the Boy Scouts.

"There is a way of returning there, but nearly everyone gives up the idea when they learn the conditions."

"I'll go, whatever the terms are," said Chemin, so excited that he thought he could hear his living heart beating in his breast again.

"Well, then, all you've got to do is to take the main road to the left on leaving Telescope Square, the road they call the Avenue of the Clearsighted. You keep straight on until you feel a desperate fatigue in your knees. Then you turn to the right. Immediately your fatigue will disappear, and this will be the sign that you are on the right road. Then once again you'll keep right on until you can no longer stand on your legs, and you'll turn, to the left this time, you understand, and the next time to the right, and so on several times. I can't tell you any more about it, but I know that these are indispensable proofs whereby they gauge the strength of character and the patience of the candidates."

"You can count on me," said the former sergeant, unconsciously drawing himself up. "I'm a reliable man."

"And you would really agree," added the keeper after a moment, "to live down there in an inferior position?"

There was a short silence during which the sergeant waited

to be told what this "inferior position" was, and the keeper to be asked it. Chemin was too proud to ask and the other too conceited to speak before he had been honored with a question. "I agree to everything," said Chemin at last.

"Well then, follow my instructions, all my instructions, you understand," said the keeper, slightly irritated at being left with all his information on the tip of his tongue.

Chemin, still standing at attention, saluted the keeper, who also stood at attention to return the salute. One was so far removed from everything, up there, and particularly from what on earth we call ridicule, that it seemed quite natural to see those two souls, without a military cap, saluting each other soldier-fashion, when Chemin was on the point of leaving for disturbing adventures.

It needed great courage for him to set out in this way along roads where he would never meet a living soul. People hardly ever ventured outside certain districts and public squares; even if one was an atheist, the dread of the mystery whose immense possibilities lay in wait all round them encouraged the souls to be as reserved and suspicious as they knew how.

Chemin advanced alone, under a sky that knew neither clouds, nor day, nor night, and seemed to have chosen for its substance and its unvarying light a kind of twilight thronged with immense, very pale stars. The silence in these regions was such that the traveler could hear the slightest thought in his head, a thing which could not help but be very disagreeable. Chemin had already been walking for a long time without feeling any fatigue, and was finally beginning to get anxious about it, when he suddenly felt in his knees such a pain that he thought he would collapse. He turned to the right and immediately felt relieved. Decidedly the keeper's information was first rate.

And now he was walking along a very narrow path, half way up the precipice of the night, between the dizziness of the heights and that of the depths. Around him were veritable rocks of sky, and silent avalanches.

Suddenly he fell into an enormous pocket of emptiness and thought he was going to roll into the bottomless abysses in the hollow embrace of Eternity. Still dazed by his fall, Chemin repeated several times: "To see my wife again, I owe her an explanation . . ."

Rather crestfallen, he kept on somehow or other, like a man who knows too much or not enough. The stars began to grow bigger still, until they became serrated full moons; it was possible now to see, close to, the whole of the celestial machinery, with what looked like luminous pulleys linking star to star.

When he had turned eleven times to right and left, he finally met some animals in a huge square. In the whole Beyond he had hitherto seen neither dog, nor cat, nor even a ladybird, and there, as though in some immense zoological garden without an enclosing wall, animals of all kinds came up and sniffed him sympathetically. With a couple of bounds, which were after all rather insolent, a tiger, and then an elephant, jumped over Chemin's head and then returned to rub themselves against him, looking casually in another direction as they did so, to show that they meant him no harm.

All the same, the creatures were looking at him rather oddly. They were most certainly disembodied beings, like himself, and weighed practically nothing. But this lightness seemed to add something particularly disquieting to their presence.

At last Chemin arrived at a place called Faithful Remembrance. It was a completely circular little place, surrounded with entrance gates on which were written names of animals: "Cats," "Birds," "Elephants," "Weasels," "Dogs," etc. As soon as he had set foot in this place, he was seized with a slight nervous trembling, impossible to control.

He met a man coming out of the entrance gate marked "Dogs," and went in that direction. The gate keeper resembled a dog clipper whom Chemin had seen one day on Earth. First he looked deep into the former teacher's eyes, down to the very root of his soul, then he showed him some colored pictures of dogs: poodles, Pekinese, a pug-dog on the knees of an old lady, a greyhound running behind a stag, pairs of New-foundlands surrounded by puppies who already had a look of devotion.

What did they expect him to do with all that? Why this family portrait?

"You fully understand," said the gate keeper, "that we can't send you on earth in the skin of a man. That would be really too easy and we should be besieged with requests. So if you're really set on it, we give you a choice between these models."

Chemin was ashamed to draw back. "I accept," he said, blushing as much as a shade can. And he held out to the gate keeper a picture of a fox terrier. They were dogs which his wife adored.

"Well then, fill in this form and sign it," said the man, with a weary air.

The paper said:

I agree to become (state the type of dog in legible writing) . . . . . *in the town of* . . . . . *for the space of* . . . . . *years* . . . . . *months* . . . . . *days.*

And, in capital letters:

AT MY OWN RISK.

Chemin scratched out *years, months,* and *days,* and wrote: *for as long as possible;* then he signed it with the determined air of a man joining the Foreign Legion.

Before leaving the gate keeper, Chemin begged him never to tell anyone of his canine adventure.

"Tell anyone!" cried the man. "Haven't you heard of the secrecy of the Intimates?" (That was what the men charged with the different services of transformation were called.) "Rest assured! We don't need to bridle our tongues; they do it for themselves."

Behind the entrance gate a sort of large Newfoundland, with human hands and cat's ears, signaled him to pass through a little low door and, once there, handed him some kind of smelling salts in a sort of bottle. He inhaled with all his might, repeating meanwhile: "To see my wife again, even with the eyes of a dog."

Thereupon Chemin found himself running along the rue des Canettes in the middle of Paris. His heart was beating so fast that he had to stop and lie down on the pavement, his tongue hanging out. He gently closed his eyes in the new-found sunlight. What a change from up there! He got to his feet again; not far from his own house, there was a mirror in his barber's window. How many times had he not looked at himself there, before going to give his lesson, to see if his clothes were all in order. And this was how he looked now. He must be about three years old. Without being a show dog, he was certainly a nice animal to look at.

Chemin's concierge, looking quite unchanged, was sitting knitting at the door of No. 27. Oh no, he would never dare lick her hand, even respectfully. He would wait till she took herself off before he entered the house.

Intoxicated with life, he couldn't decide where to go, nor exactly what to do with all this happiness and, to keep himself in countenance, he ran along frowning anxiously, as if an exacting master were expecting him at a definite time.

Some children saw him and threw stones at him. He fled charitably, to avoid biting them. His long tail, very white and quite new, followed him everywhere, continually calling attention to him among all the fox terriers of Paris, whose tails were docked.

"Why ever did they make me come to Earth with such a compromising appendage?" he said to himself. "They ought to have done the necessary up there."

In the shadow of a main entrance, he cut his tail off at the root with his teeth. It was very distressing to experience pain again. And the flowing blood was making a great mess. After all, a soul is much cleaner. All the same, he liked the taste of the blood; it was not at all insipid, as blasé people asserted.

The day passed slowly and the concierge was still at the

door. The street lamps began to shine. He had to hide more and more; the policeman on night duty, much more alarming than those on during the day, were already about under their terrible hoods, heavy bodies with no souls.

Chemin began to consider his present plight. No doubt there were plenty of dogs walking in Paris, as he was, on paws that had come from the other world. But how was he to recognize them? To be authorized to return to Earth you had to be a modest animal, exactly like all the others, with your secret stuck in your throat like a chicken bone.

At last Chemin's wife appeared. How pretty she was, even better than from up there! Obeying the impulse of his heart, he rushed toward her. She took him in her arms, hugged him to her breast as though to express its mystery, and then put him down on the pavement. It was over already.

He followed her. She was as attractive from behind as in front. When she went into a shop, he remained humbly at the door. When she came out, she pretended not to recognize him. With a look, he did his best to say to her: "But you are my mistress. I've never loved anyone but you." He nibbled at her skirt.

"Come now, be reasonable."

How could he make her understand that he was reason itself? "How difficult it is to get oneself adopted!" sighed the dog, still new to the job. It was no good just behaving correctly. You follow someone for a bit, they stroke you and rub your ears in a friendly way, they take your muzzle in their hands and gaze into your eyes with their faces close to yours, and you think you have made a friend. And then, if you're only a dog, they shut the door in your face immediately afterward, as though they recognized an enemy.

He suddenly remembered that, in the house where he lived before he died, it was forbidden to keep dogs. To avoid giving way to despair, he rushed all the same in the direction of his former dwelling and climbed the five flights as fast as a great runaway horse. He was preparing to wait for his former wife on the mat when he remembered that, when she went on short errands, she thought it was all right to leave the door only apparently closed behind her, so as not to have to get out her keys. He went in, pushing the door behind him, but so clumsily that he shut it.

"There's a nice way to get myself well received," he thought.

He ran from the dining room to the kitchen, and from there to the balcony. He saw his photo, as a sergeant in the Rifles, standing on a cupboard in an ebony frame with a cluster of artificial pansies on the side of it, the whole thing looking most effective.

He was still gazing at himself when he heard his wife's footsteps. As always, she was lucky. He heard her thanking the concierge for having opened the door for her.

When the young woman entered the dining room she saw the dog determinedly licking the glass of her husband's photo.

"But I know that dog, he follows me everywhere," she said, taking his head between her hands. "Poor brute, you don't realize I'm going to have to put you outside. Oh, his tail's all mangled!"

She washed his wound carefully.

The next day she sadly showed him the door. He pretended not to understand. She insisted. So did he. She ended by keeping him. And when she took him out, before passing in front of the concierge's lodge, she hid him in the string shopping bag.

"Your mummie's very glad to have you near her, my little man. Now then, don't bark, you know very well that in this building one isn't allowed to say one's a dog."

It had been a splendid welcome. All said and done, the only thing that Chemin reproached his wife with was undressing before him, under his very nose, as though he had been a mere china dog.

One evening, a man entered the room, a big, fat man, vulgarity itself in a lounge suit with some flowers in his hand.

The one-time teacher said to himself that he had seen that mug somewhere. He searched his human memory for a time, and then his dog's memory, and finally cried: "But it's our butcher!"

The couple were now sitting on the divan. The man brought out of his pocket a box of sticky sweets. "It's easier to eat sticky sweets than to make conversation," thought the dog, who never took his eyes off the butcher. "You suck, and crunch, and swallow, and then begin again. And that's all you have to do to get yourself liked!" Not to mention that he was eating three to her one. Funny way of giving presents!

It looked to Chemin as though he were kissing the young woman on the mouth. And he was still hesitating whether to believe in this kiss when the man gave her another one, which was a long confirmation of the first. He clasped her round the waist with a satisfied air and without surprise, as though this feminine flesh had always belonged to him.

"Stop it now!"

"But I'm only just beginning, beautiful! You don't really suppose I've taken this trouble for nothing?"

"For nothing," thought Chemin. "What a coarse creature!"

"Let's go into my room," said she. "I don't want the dog to look at me when I'm half-naked."

The man she had chosen, a red-faced, sluggish man, was concerned only with his own pleasure. He would happily have embraced his wife before fifty different portraits of Chemin, and in front of his row of pipes, and his sergeant's tunic with his decorations, and his blackboard, and the hoops of his pupils.

"All the same," thought Chemin, "I think she might have found someone better among my former comrades."

The butcher came back two days later. They had dinner. The conversation languished. They busied themselves with the dog.

"You ought to teach him to retrieve." And he threw one of

Elise's gloves. The dog would not leave his corner. The butcher was about to get angry when he fell asleep on his dinner napkin.

She took the fox terrier in her arms and looked at him quite close, nose to nose. Then something deep within him, something profoundly canine for all that, forced Chemin to make eyes at this woman.

Toward midnight they went into the bedroom. In despair, the former teacher went to sleep as quickly as he could in the dining room. "Dog, bitch, son of a dog," he thought, and went over all those sad oaths incorporating the word which now described him in the eyes of all the world. In his dream he gave vent to a long-drawn howl at death. The enlaced couple would have needed only one of their four ears to hear that lugubrious *hoo! hoo! hoo!* coming from the dining room. The dog was released from his nightmare by the man in his underdrawers, with one garter on calves that were hairy as caterpillars. He took Chemin by the scruff of his neck and threw him into a cupboard cluttered with old shoes, boxes, and trifling objects which had once belonged to him.

From that day on, the lover—for one definitely had to call the vulgar butcher by that charming name—adopted the habit of shutting the dog in the cupboard, with a kick to hurry him in. Finally he stopped calling the former teacher anything but Cupboard, and even Cupboard-and-a-Half when he was in a good mood.

Chemin would perhaps have gone far away if he had not, in spite of everything, spent some happy hours with his former wife when she was using her sewing machine. The gentle mechanical noise of it, and the tapping of her little foot which he let himself freely admire, soothed his canine solitude. Or sometimes a pretty white thread caught on Elise's skirt, and he would sit and gaze at it as though it were an earthly miracle.

"You're a bad wife, you are," thought Chemin, "when I think how I was prepared for anything for the joy of seeing you again. The joy indeed, I like that!"

"Where would we be if I didn't work so as to give you something to eat?" went on Elise. "What would you say if I offered you an empty saucer?"

"That's true," thought Chemin, suddenly full of shame. "It's she who feeds me. Even if I do only eat scraps, she still has to see to it that there are some."

He thought of the sheep dogs who round up flocks; they earn their living. And watchdogs, described as "fierce," in villas on the outskirts of Paris; they earn it too. But as for him, condemned as he was to be a clandestine dog, how could he think of earning his living? He had to consent to be fed and lodged, giving nothing in return but a tongue moist with gratitude.

It vexed the butcher that he had not yet learned how to win the dog's friendship. One day he said to the widow:

"Guess what I've brought in this basket? It's for Cupboard."

The man undid the basket. Inside it there was a bitch.

"It belongs to a colleague," he said. "You see, I thought we mustn't be selfish, and that we ought to see that our little Cupboard has some pleasure."

He made the bitch jump out of the basket. She needed no persuading for she was making all sorts of advances. She was all prinked for love, with a pink bow at her neck. The former sergeant pretended not to notice anything. When the bitch insisted, he bit her very hard on the leg.

"Oh, the brute!" roared the lover. "He's made my bitch bleed. I'll teach you manners! Just you wait a moment!" And he struck him with a whip, which he brought out of a pocket you would not have thought was deep enough.

The widow took the side of her dog. "What, you still stand up for him? Into the cupboard, Cupboard!" And, clasping his mistress round the waist, he went into the bedroom. The bitch followed, her bell tinkling.

"So that's what metempsychosis means!" thought the dog in the cupboard. If he could ever have imagined that one day he would have had a bone to pick with that word, one of those learned words that come from the Greek and seem as though they ought to shed honor on the person of whom they are used. Ah, you never know, when you see words in a dictionary, whether one fine day one or other of them won't detach itself and stick to you like an infernal label. They have such an insidious way of inserting themselves in your life. He thought of the names of diseases, and of words to do with jurisprudence, and the sciences, occult or otherwise. Men use words, he thought, but the words get even with them.

The lover, who had to go to the market, left before daylight, taking the bitch in the basket. He was still cross, as if it had been he who was not wanted.

The next day, Chemin wanted to leave, but Cupboard was anxious to stay. Chemin had turned against the place, while Cupboard, in spite of everything, clung to it. And Elise kept on saying in his ear: "Call me mummie. D'you know, I always longed to have a child from Paul?" He had returned to earth to clear up a misunderstanding and here he was merely aggravating it by his presence.

"It's enough to drive one mad," said Chemin to himself. As a rule, this statement alone is enough to dispel the poison inside one; but in Chemin's case it began to obsess him and take on a terrible significance for him. "Ah, why did I come down here again?" thought the man-dog. "The dead have nothing but putrefaction to offer. It is the only gift they know how to make properly."

For some days past he would gladly have bitten his wife, for choice on the calf, whose plumpness and whiteness tempted his canine teeth and heated his blood. He knew the place very well from having caressed it in the old days; it was as smooth as one could desire. But why not bite the butcher instead? It wasn't cowardice, but the idea of sinking his fangs into that dirty, male meat disgusted the dog.

Madness! He remembered how having read that that disorder is marked by a period of sadness like that which he had noticed in himself, and by a change of habits, "against which one should always be on one's guard," say the textbooks. That was it all right. Had he not, the other day, taken his piece of meat under the cupboard, set on eating it there? And in the cupboard, had he not torn to pieces and even chewed half of one of his own shoes, which he had no reason to feel cross with? Yes, it was madness, born of the dire combination of man and dog in him.

"You never say good morning to me nowadays, my pet," said Elise to him. "You've quite changed."

"Ah, wife, why do you look at me with such utter trust? It will cost you dear in the end. Today you are sewing a spangled bodice which makes me tremble in every limb. It glitters before my eyes with a kind of ferocity! Yet there you sit, working so calmly!"

Every one of Cupboard's teeth had grown alive and independent and clamored for its share of Elise. The four canines cried loudest.

One day, in an attempt to banish any criminal idea, he tried, in an atmosphere of absolute purity, to imagine Elise as though he were seeing her for the first time. And, caught in his own toils, he went toward her, ready to lick her hand in all innocence when, from the depths of his teacher's memory, rose the words: "Licking is sufficient to cause madness." Swiftly he took refuge under the cupboard, hiding his tongue and his fatal saliva.

"You poor creature, whatever is the matter with you?"

"Don't go and strengthen the bonds between us," he thought. "You'd much better arm yourself with the broom, you haven't a moment to lose!"

The more affection she showed him, the more abundant became the dog's poisonous saliva. In vain did he try to swallow it. There was a great deal more than he could consume.

Elise wanted to drag Cupboard from under the cupboard to examine him and take him to the vet. She took a stick and pushed him as hard as she could to make him come out. The dog resisted in vain, and out he came, his face close to that of Elise, who was repeating: "But what's the matter, whatever's the matter with you?"

In a single bound he jumped through the open window, grazing a balcony (the third floor or the second?). That deadened his fall and he found himself limping and bleeding on the streets of Paris. In spite of that, he set off at a rapid pace, as if the madness were giving him unexpected strength. He made now for the school where he once taught. How often had he not, by means of drawings on the blackboard, put his pupils on guard against mad dogs, and now there he was exactly answering his own description of them. Before dying, he felt he must show himself in class with all the force of an object lesson.

All of a sudden, forgetting where he was going, he hesitated which road to follow. Someone seized the opportunity to hit him. The whole town was after him. Though they might throw iron bars, rocks, or even paving stones at him, what was left of the teacher in him prevented him from biting anyone.

He had received so many blows that he fell. As he lost blood, the madness also left him. Elise arrived, hatless, having rushed downstairs at top speed. Panting, she rushed up and tried to take the dog in her arms.

"Stand back!" a policeman called to her. "Can't you see he's mad?"

"He's spitting blood just like we do," said an old lady.

Elise didn't want to leave the dog, whose eyes were now closing in spite of himself. It was quite true to say that he saw himself dying, with a threefold vision: the vision of the dog, of the man, and of his wife, who gazed at him, her eyes full of tears.

Up above, he handed back his disguise in the place they called "the cloakroom," and immediately got back his human appearance, including his nose which certainly suited him to perfection.

ORPHEUS

Before his day, the wind in the foliage made no sound, the sea sleeked its waves in complete silence, rain fell on roofs without a murmur, and people were always remarking on the muteness of waterfalls. Nature was waiting for her first poet.

Birds used to look at you with their songs lying inert at the back of their beaks. It was Orpheus who unlocked the throats of the nightingales. And they still sing today as they did in the days of the first poet, recording the time when he came.

If the fish still remain silent, it is because they lived even then in the water, and so could not hear the poet's voice. But the mermaids, whose only fishy part is their tails, were able to profit by his lesson. It was thanks to Orpheus that the swallows learned how to set about bringing news from the horizon. And if he had not died so young, he would have gone from space to space, giving a voice to the moon, the sun, and the stars, and even to those stars that we shall not see for centuries and centuries to come. But hear him speak:

"My father was an eminent waterway. One day Calliope, who was to become my mother, was blissfully bathing in this river. Call as they might to her from the bank, she stayed in for hours, clasped in the delightful arms of the stream.

"I am the fruit of that union—half-carnal and half-aquatic, half-white and half-glaucous, half-silence (my mother remained taciturn right up to my birth) and half-music. I have poetry in my blood.

"My river of a father reflected towns, skies, and clouds from his source to his mouth. He mingled with light as well as with darkness. An incorrigible walker, fussy like all rivers, he insisted on rising every day in the mountains, following the same bends, and throwing himself into the sea. And the next day he would begin all over again, in spite of the objections of my mother, who would have preferred him to be sedentary, if not stay-at-home. That is why I like walking in the country, singing as I go, though, unlike my father, I rarely go the same way."

One day when Orpheus was singing to the soft strains of his lyre, a lion lay down at his feet. And so modest was the poet that he innocently thought: "Just a coincidence." The lion gazed at the holder of the lyre with a gentleness so musical that it seemed to be native to him. But it was all owing to the poet. "I thank you," said the lion, textually, with a look which sprang from his wild beast's deepest depths, "for having so exactly expressed what I, who can only roar, have long felt." Then, still with his look, he added: "There is nothing finer than to lay aside one's ferocity in full view of everyone."

Embarrassed by such eloquent eyes, Orpheus lowered his lids and began to sing. The lion listened to him with such an honest face that some lambs lay down on his shadow. When he was getting near the end, the poet signed to the shepherd to come and collect his woolly ones, before the lion descended from the pure heights to which the music had raised him.

It was extremely awkward not to be able to sing without eliciting such a volume of admiration from all manner of beasts. "How much I prefer the refusal of the trees and stones to leave their surroundings," thought Orpheus. "Immobility is a proof that things have learned wisdom. It is their white beard. Once upon a time everything on the planet moved. That was the age when geology was conquering the world. Every land, every rock, and every mountain was movable. In our time nature, thank the gods, has settled down."

On a country walk one day, Orpheus was beginning to compose some verses again when he heard behind him a noise like roots being torn up: he was being followed by an avenue of poplars. He fell silent and the trees at once stood still. He pronounced two or three words, just to see. The poplars took a step, only one, but so full of admiration that the poet, red with shame, decided to keep silent for the whole day.

The next day, he began to play again, and again the poplars followed him. Men came down from the mountains and goats from the rocks. Then the rocks themselves left the parent rock and started off in the direction whence that music came. The snow left the heights to seek out the poet and, under the influence of the poetry, did not melt in the sun. The sucking infant let go of its mother's breast and turned round to hear better, the assassin's knife was suspended and grew rusty in the air, the migrating bird alighted on a branch, and the traveler sat down, while the trees formed a circle round Orpheus.

Although he did not sing loud and often contented himself with little more than a murmur, the music from the world within him spread far and wide, suppressing distances and creating waves of sound which rippled on again until they reached the furthest spaces of the air and the heavens. And the mermaids flocked round him, begging in disarmingly humble voices: "O sir, a little kiss, if you please."

Then Orpheus hid his face in his hands and wept and cursed himself. "What a wretched thing it is," he thought, "thus to disturb the most sacred foundations of nature. It's so beautiful when the snow remains on the mountain tops and the mermaids in the sea, when the trees obey their roots, the wild beasts their ferocity, and men their passions. And there I go interrupting the course of destiny with my poor music, while my art has repercussions in the very bowels of the earth. Happy are those whom only themselves and the gods hear!"

So as no longer to see anything around him, Orpheus decided to sing only on moonless nights. But thereupon even the shape of his lyre was indiscreetly revealed to him in the darkness by the fireflies which came from everywhere to settle on it.

For several weeks the poet preserved complete silence. He scarcely dared breathe. And first on one day then on another, by means of patient chords at very long intervals, Orpheus gave nature to understand that, when he sang, everything must remain in its place. Nature took the hint and Orpheus was able to start singing again as he walked on the sunlit grass or along the stony mountain paths.

"I only like miracles when they are hidden," he thought. "And if I chose Eurydice for a wife it was because she didn't raise her arms to heaven like the other young girls whenever I began to sing. She kept her emotion to herself."

But Orpheus was so much in love with music that it made him forget his wife. And she was loved in secret by a brutal shepherd, called Aristheus, who had long since killed all music in himself. Once when he was pursuing Eurydice among the lagoons and the reeds, she was stung to death by a serpent, born of the night itself and embodying the surprises and treachery of the night.

Thereupon Orpheus rushed thither from very far off, guided by his heart, which was at last awakened. Stirred by the incense of the funeral rites, his love finally shook off its torpor. Stricken with silence before the inert body of his wife, the poet decided to hold his peace forever, not even replying to questions put to him by the gods. All music, every word, seemed to him henceforth a profanation.

The gods could not long endure being deprived of that voice, which was so pure that it linked earth to heaven with no effort and with the greatest tact.

Orpheus was given permission to go and fetch his wife, restored from the dead, and to bring her from the underworld, going before her with his gaze fixed on the door of the Shades. But when he was within a few paces of deliverance, the most human of poets could not prevent himself, in spite of the divine command, from turning his head toward his beloved. At first he did not see that his gesture had made his wife disappear, but almost immediately he began to sing a song so sad that after it there was no longer any place in the world for Eurydice.

Cruelly enlightened by his own music, he grew desperate at

having loved his wife so ill, and in his frenzy this poet, who could infuse life into rocks, hastily put together some verses which came swiftly to him from the far reaches of his mind, in an attempt, in spite of everything, to set the heart of Eurydice, which had turned into stone, beating once more.

But already the wind of death was blowing Orpheus far away from the underworld. The Bacchantes, who hated music and poetry, which slake the thirst of the senses without feeding their lust, had stationed themselves at intervals at the exit from the underworld, to watch for the poet by the wayside, like a horrible cordon of police with vindictive nipples. As beautiful as they were fierce, they thought that if the first of them did not succeed in seducing Orpheus, the second would, or the third, or the twentieth, who was concealing two daggers.

And when Orpheus passed in front of them without even seeing them, they all hurled themselves on him at once and cut his throat on the seashore.

Though he was now only a severed but still musical head and a floating lyre, the poet continued to sing in a low voice of his love for Eurydice. Many hours after his death his lips went on murmuring new images and beautiful sounds which none but poets to come could hear.

The lyre floated close by, still anxious to respond; but since there were no hands to pluck it, moved by the intermittent breath of the spirit it now played of itself and as if from memory, a memory in shreds. And sometimes it drifted off a little on the swell of the sea, and at other times it drew close enough to the head of Orpheus to touch it.

THE RAPE OF EUROPA

It was Juno's habit to wander every morning over the slopes of Olympus shouting: "Fidelity!" Everyone answered: "Fidelity!" And the beasts bellowed or mewed their agreement.

"You might at least answer like the rest," she said one day to Jupiter.

"I did answer."

"So low that I didn't hear anything."

"You know very well that if I shout it starts a thunderstorm. And the mortals are complaining that they've had a lot of rain lately."

Juno went on her way, still shouting: "Fidelity!" The satyrs who had ventured on to the slopes of Olympus answered without hesitation: "Fidelity, of course," and Juno returned home thinking that all was well.

That particular morning the goddess had heard it said that her husband, in search of new adventures, was about to metamorphose himself once again. He had been discovered closely examining all sorts of animals before deciding. Not having forgotten the recent affair of Leda, Juno, the moment she caught sight of a swan, or of a goose, a turkey, or a pigeon by itself, would go up to it and say on the off-chance: "Aren't you ashamed to be up to your pranks again?" And since the startled but innocent creature could not answer, she would go on:

"I'll wring your neck for you, and we'll soon see if that doesn't squeeze the name of your mistress out of your illustrious beak!"

Then, realizing her mistake: "Oh, I'm going crazy with it all! The most insignificant woman on earth is happier than I. She can keep an eye on her man. But just try and do as much with a gentleman who's omnipotent. If the fancy takes him, there isn't a speck of dust or a star or an insect that can't hide my husband. I wish I were a loose woman so that I could revenge myself on him twenty times a day. But the trouble is I only like things that are absolutely innocent: women with child by their husband, the cries of legitimate new-born babes, a mother suckling her twins, the same mother blowing the noses of her other children, the smell of freshly washed linen, and pots of ambrosia neatly ranged in the larder."

She was also fond of whispering advice, whose utter uselessness she knew, in the ears of young girls on the threshold of their bridal chamber. It was her one vice.

As for Jupiter, after marrying Themis, then Eurynome, then Ceres, his own sister, then Mnemosyne, then Latona, another of his sisters, and finally Juno, who was also his sister, he thought to himself: "These immortals are always a bit dreary. They know they've got all time before them and so they never take the trouble to behave like real women once in a while."

And so, hidden behind a little wood, he said: "White!" and became white, "Bull!" and became bull, "In the prime of life!" and he was a bull three years old. He then bellowed so as to get the feel of his new skin and its contents, and set off down the slopes of Olympus at a brisk trot. Congratulating himself on his new disguise, he decided, as on former occasions, to test the reliability of his incognito by passing close to Juno.

"There's a well-proportioned bull!" she said.

"That's right, look me over well," thought Jupiter, "you'll never catch on."

The bull bellowed and, just to show that he felt entirely at ease, the hypocrite urinated in front of Juno.

"There's a good boy," said she. "I'm not at all worried by you. I know very well Jupiter would never dare change himself into a bull after that time when I changed myself into a heifer. After all, my husband's hardly as disrespectful as all that! All the same, one really should never let one's brother marry one, even if he is Jupiter. What does a sister matter? When you've all been brought up together, you think nothing of deceiving one another."

The young Europa was playing on the shore with some friends. The pure white bull drew near her and then came gently to a standstill, like a monument to innocence and timidity. Full of wonder, the young girl moved away from her friends.

"Why do you want to make me take you for a bull?" she asked. "You're nothing of the sort. A lamb, that's what you are. And I'm going to prove it to you by getting on your back."

"See what comes of concealing one's intentions," thought Jupiter.

"Now go for a little gallop."

The bull did not wait to be asked twice, and galloped along the shore. He was so dazed with happiness under his pure white skin that he got into the wrong register, and neighed instead of lowing. But the young girl was so joyful that she did not even notice.

In the distance, Juno could be heard on her morning round: "Fidelity! Fidelity!"

Jupiter was pleased with his new skin and with the whole disguise. He was not one of those impulsive gods who become half this and half that, centaurs or ostrilions. All the same, he thought, if he was to remain a bull, his considerable weight and the clumsiness of his gestures would be a great drawback when it came to courting the young Europa. Why had he chosen such a heavy animal for this first encounter? Would it not have been better to be a lamb or a butterfly? "But what if I do want to be bestial, haven't I every right?" "You certainly have." "And what if I want to crush her with the whole weight of my taurine body?" "You can, of course, but it won't be very pretty." "And if I don't care a bit whether it's pretty or not?" "Be careful, or you may spoil your own pleasure!"

"Well I never!" said Juno, toiling up the slopes of Olympus. "Everyone's talking of this bull, and I'm the only one who didn't recognize my husband." In her fury she opened all the gates of heaven to let the clouds out.

"There she goes again," thought Jupiter, "making it rain on my pleasures. Well, bull though I am, I'll show her I'm not afraid of water."

When Europa found herself suddenly in the sea, she began to utter loud cries. The bull pitched and rolled a lot. To reassure her, he turned a human face toward her at the end of his bull's neck, but this only frightened her the more. So he became completely taurine again but, as his cargo of living flesh was really shifting about too much, he grew some strong fins on his flanks and thereafter advanced smoothly over the waves.

Europa, thus abducted, thought herself mad, and not mad at all, daring and absolutely safe, adventurous and wonderfully prudent, while the nuptial bull floundered gravely along in the sea, where his august slaver added to the splendor of the foam.

All at once the false ruminant halted, and the god took his place. He clasped the young girl in a long embrace.

"By Zeus," said Europa, "you have dishonored me."

"By Zeus," said he, "I am honor itself, I confer honor. Nothing about me can dishonor you. Even your modesty is safeguarded. I am the earth and the sky, the past and the future, and what is more I love you."

True, Jupiter felt slightly ashamed at using such heavy guns for his conquests. But shame did not last long with him, any more than with the other gods, and a majestic good humor very soon ousted all other feelings.

"And now what are you going to do with me?" said the young girl.

"Nothing more and nothing less, you are going to be my wife."

They were embracing again when Jupiter suddenly felt himself being prodded and, as it were, hoisted up by some three-pronged thing.

"Who dares?" roared the god of Olympus.

It was Neptune's trident.

"How could I have known?" asked the sea king. "How could I have supposed the earth and the sky weren't big enough to hide your affairs? You might at least have warned me."

As a matter of fact, Neptune had recognized his brother quite well. That exquisite girl, and the great bed of foam near that bull's hide, which still looked alive . . . But he had wanted to make the point that the sea belonged to him.

"What a bore he is with this watery element of his," said Jupiter, moving away. "Europa, you shall be my island wife. We'll have a home of our own. And we'll make love on dry land."

Europa was still wondering what these words meant when she found herself beside the king of the gods in the middle of a quite new little archipelago which had just risen from the sea. There were palm trees on it, and birds and domestic animals, and a beautiful, pure white house at whose door stood smiling slaves, the whole thing still dripping with sea water and awaiting orders.

Jupiter would have been very late back for supper that night if he had not hidden the sun behind the clouds and made it stand still for two hours. It was his way of putting the clock back. And it was so well done that not a single astronomer nor a single housewife noticed it. Neither did the farm laborers. It happened when they were getting the hay in and they all said to each other: "Who would have thought we should have finished it today? We certainly have put our backs into it!"

When the king of the gods got home to dinner on the summit of Olympus, he had made up his mind to reply shortly: "Divine labors," if ever his wife asked him what he had been doing. But Juno was not there to receive him, and the King of the Gods realized from the stubborn silence of his servants that his chief spouse knew all about his adventure.

"After all, I really don't see why I bother with these disguises. Haven't I every right?"

All the same, he decided to be more cunning in the future and, by way of a beginning, not to give the snowy-footed Juno the present he had brought back for her: a pure white bedside mat, his own bull's hide.

ANTHONY OF THE DESERT

Once upon a time in Egypt, when the hermit Anthony had a dead body to bury, he heard a persistent scratching at his door. It was two lions.

"Pray be so good as to enter, gentlemen," he said with ceremony.

But the lions remained rooted on either side of the door, and the hermit was obliged to let them dig the grave, which they did very quickly with their front paws. Then, working faster still with their hind paws, they shoveled the earth back over the corpse, not even leaving Anthony time to lie down beside the dead man to give him a little guidance on the threshold of eternal night.

The Nile crocodiles were just as zealous in serving the hermit. Whenever Anthony approached the river, they quarreled as to which should have the honor of taking him over on its back.

In spite of all that, the devil did not relax his grip on that beautiful soul. "I grant you the animals are on your side," said he, "but what of that? Does that make you any more worthy to be what they call an anchorite? Just take a look at yourself in this glass and you'll soon see if that ill-spent youth of yours is a thing of the past or not." The accursed one had planned things so that the hermit should see a pig in the mirror. But Anthony stood up to him, and bought a real pig, which at once began to follow him everywhere.

Nevertheless, it was clear that the hermit was not completely reassured. If anyone looked him in the eye and asked him maliciously, "How are you getting on?" the simple soul would be certain to admit, "Oh, I'd be all right if it weren't for my temptations."

And off he would go, so skinny and dry that you wondered how it was that the desert sun did not set him alight.

Anthony loved his pig as someone who has not yet been able to show all his powers and must be encouraged by a full and frank friendship. It upset him greatly when he sometimes heard people making remarks like: "Fancy a reserved man like that keeping such company!" or else: "Since the whole point of a pig is to turn into pig-meat, one ought to see to it that the creatures fatten well and quickly."

Every morning the hermit spent over an hour polishing his pig until it fairly radiated cleanliness. But the pig, ungrateful and resplendent, always looked as though he thought Anthony was not doing enough of it, and he would often rub himself against his master's legs to beg for further attentions. More than once during their walks the pig exaggerated his fatigue, or pretended to limp, so as to get Anthony to carry him on his back. The hermit looked upon the terrific effort that this caused him as a real godsend, a cheap way of doing penance. Or perhaps the creature, pretending to be absent-minded, would begin by eating Anthony's meal before turning his attention to the contents of his own bowl. The pig even managed to convey to his master that it was rather for the poor quadruped to sleep in the bed and for Anthony to lie on the ground.

However, the devil still did not admit himself defeated. Proud of his reputation as a pander, he found no difficulty in introducing the most zealous of his women into the hermit's dreams. One night, when the wretched man was obsessed past bearing by detestable thoughts, he jumped out of bed and went so far as to swallow three great spoonfuls of desert sand in the hope of thus obtaining some relief.

"Ah me, the whole Sahara would not suffice," said he, as he lay down again. And for a long time he smote himself on his chest, which rang like the honest chest it was. "It's no good, you're done for," he said to himself, "go on all fours, you vile beast! Nay rather, go and take pattern from your pig, abase yourself before him."

The pig was not to be found at the end of the room where he usually spent the night. Following his tracks, Anthony heard a satisfied snuffling some little distance away. Pushing open a door, in the light of his lantern he saw his pet lying beside a sow.

The hermit was disappointed, but not for long. "After all, *he* hasn't made any vows. One can hardly blame him, he's only obeying his nature."

All the same, Anthony felt a trifle sore with his pig. But was it really the quadruped's fault? Anthony had tended and beautified and fattened him too much. It was hardly astonishing that he attracted the attention and desire of females. So when next day the pig came up for Anthony to groom him, the hermit said to him: "Shift for yourself!"

After this he resolved to take the pig with him on a great journey through the purifying desert. When the moment of departure came, the pig, who had noticed certain preparations, presented himself with his sow.

"What do you expect me to do with *that?*" said Anthony.

Never before had he spoken to the pig in such a tone. He followed it up with a few blows of his stick on the sow's back. Then off they set, leaving the female behind.

They plunged into the treeless desert, where the only shade was the thin but fraternal shadow cast at long intervals by an occasional anchorite. "Sand plus sand equals tranquillity," said the hermit. "Hurrah for the absence of females, meat, vegetables, and every blessed thing! Nothing here to prevent me from meditating upon the heavens and adoring them. But I certainly did hit the sow rather too hard just now. To be honest, dismissing her as an invention of the devil was really too convenient."

As for the pig, he felt that no good would come of that non-edible immensity. "My hardy stomach may be able to digest things that others despise," he thought, "but all the same I can scarcely eat my shadow on the sand." So after two or three miles he silently retraced his steps. Anthony felt so purified by the desert wind that he turned round to call on the pig to witness his exaltation. Only after considerable trouble did he find him, a long way away, behind a tuft of scorched grasses. The animal was breathing with difficulty. He had been stung in the foot by a serpent. Anthony's astonishment slowly gave place to great anguish. Afraid of causing the pig suffering, he treated him only with prayers and a stream of saliva, which he thought would be efficacious since it came from the depths of his own pure heart. The animal watched Anthony with an eye which had become sharp as a needle and, like a needle, penetrating. It was pitiful to see that eye, whose only hope of becoming once more the eye of a pig in perfect health depended on Anthony-the-awkward. And the anchorite said to himself: "Good heavens, how swiftly this disaster has overtaken us!"

He fully realized that there were now three of them in the desert: the pig, the poison, and himself; and of the three only one was visibly active, enlarging its domain and striving, in the dark labyrinth of the blood, to reach the very heart of the animal.

The foot continued to swell painfully under the poor man's despairing saliva. He knew that he ought to have cut it to the quick with his knife. But the mere sight of the blade made not only the pig but Anthony himself utter cries which left them both without courage.

It was at that moment that the sow, seized with a presentiment, caught up with the pig after a great gallop which made her dugs dance madly. She set to work to suck the wound, spit out the poison, and rub the painful foot with her snout to restore the circulation of the blood. The pig endured this treatment without a murmur. His look said to the sow: "Without you, brave female, I should have been done for."

"It's plain I'm good for nothing," thought Anthony.

"Oh, don't say that!" replied the pig and the sow by their significant silence. "It's just that you're not good at nursing serpent stings, that's all."

Anthony now realized that from then on he could not separate the pig from his companion. And they all three turned back to journey toward less deserted regions, where the hermit thought he might make himself useful. It sometimes happened that this real specialist in diabolical matters was called in consultation from a considerable distance. On one such occasion he had revealed two horns hidden under the turban of a naked little Negro boy, who was playing with some village children, and the accursed one, who had had all the trouble of the metamorphosis for nothing, had to vanish on the spot without more ado.

When Anthony arrived in a village with the pig and the sow, all the pigs went to meet him, and fêted their fellows. The swineherds came too, as was right and proper. But the pork butchers also insisted on considering the anchorite as their protector. "Stand back, pork butchers, Anthony would rather starve," he would have said to them, if he had not immediately afterward thought: "Forgive them, after all they're men."

For the villagers of the desert, the arrival of Anthony among them was often the sole event of the year. And at night the whole village would turn out to spy on the hermit's tormented slumbers. The thing was that he had rather a comic way of sleeping with his fist in his mouth, ready to bite it in the hope that the physical pain would drive away the too alluring maidens of his dreams.

One night, someone placed in the anchorite's bed a doll made of sand and crudely painted, supposed to represent a woman of ill fame. Anthony saw it when he woke up, but he was so innocent he took it for the image of a new-born babe, and vowed he would never again part from that little girl of sand, brought to him by the wind of the desert. She would see to it that his own feelings remained innocent. But the villagers tittered when they saw him set off again with his dry doll in his arms, followed by a pig with a sow trotting behind, big with young and making no attempt to conceal it.

The saint was the last to notice the threat in the sow's belly, visible on every side. "Let us shelter over there to await the event," he said to his followers, heading for an abandoned hut where a learned man had died surrounded by his books. His gleaming skeleton was still sitting in the attitude of an attentive reader.

That same day, in a heap of papyrus at the dead man's feet, Anthony discovered a treatise on the breeding of pigs. Opening it, he read: "The sow is extremely voracious; she often devours her young. One must therefore always be on the alert, especially in the case of the primiparous."

"Is she primiparous?" Anthony asked himself anxiously. "Oh dear, how insufficiently informed one always is!"

He went on with his reading: "If the number of young exceeds the number of teats, it will be as well to sacrifice the weakest ones. This is a wise precaution."

He considered the sow's serene belly. There must be an incalculable number of piglets inside it. And here was science as well as charity ordering that he kill several of them—he who lived on nothing but roots, so as not to cause blood to flow!

"Ah," he thought, "the longer one lives the more confusing it becomes!" And he fell on his knees, hoping to see more clearly.

When he had finished praying, he saw a kind of cloud at the door of the hut. It was not like other clouds, always on the move. This one was obviously waiting for someone.

"Climb into it!" said a voice within him.

"Do nothing of the kind!" retorted another.

"Didn't I tell you to climb in?" cried an angel's voice, outside him this time.

The saint climbed into the cloud. It was so comfortable inside that Anthony would have blushed for it if the cloud had given him time. But already, one inside the other, they were rising into the sky, which seemed eager to take the anchorite to its bosom.

It was not yet the hour of his death; he was flying over the Mediterranean. Faithful as a dog, swift as a bird, woolly as a sheep, as full of solicitude as a man, his cloud scudded along at a great rate toward the capital of Catalonia, keeping clear of the other clouds, who would have liked to sniff it as it passed, to find out what was going on.

The airy vehicle set the hermit down in the courtyard of the town hall, where he soon learned why he had been brought there. The devil had entered into the Queen of Catalonia and her children, and it was hoped that Anthony would rid them of him. It was the king and his court who had managed, by dint of prayer, to detach a cloud from the Egyptian sky and put it at the anchorite's disposal for the journey to Barcelona.

But just when the hermit was about to enter the royal apartments, someone tugged at the edge of his sackcloth.

"Bless my soul, where do you spring from?" said the saint, recognizing his pig and the sow.

They had taken advantage of one of the anchorite's ecstasies to climb into a dark corner of the cloud, where the sow had given birth to four enormous piglets, of which three were perfectly formed. The fourth, which had neither eyes nor feet, she held in her mouth and presented to the hermit as if it were a reproach.

The provost wanted to chase away the intruders, but Anthony, quickly taking his hand, made a sign of the cross with it over the new-born piglet at the place where the eyes and feet should have been. And immediately the little pig, eyes twinkling, began to scamper all over the place to show his gratitude. It was Anthony's soul which had done it all, so dexterous had it become.

After he had cured the king's family, the anchorite returned to Egypt by cloud with his animals, and soon after became known to everyone as St. Anthony of the Desert. But it must be admitted that, even before his journey to Catalonia, more than one keen-sighted Christian had already drawn attention to a circle of gold, more luminous every day, which surrounded the hermit's head, and which children standing on chairs, and robbers in the middle of the night, tried in vain to steal from him.

THE OX AND THE ASS
OF THE MANGER

The ass, led by Joseph, bore the Virgin along the road to Bethlehem. She weighed little, being full of nothing but the future within her.

The ox followed, by himself.

On reaching the city, the travelers made their way into a deserted stable, and Joseph at once set to work.

"These men really are astonishing," thought the ox, "the things they manage to do with their hands and arms! Those objects are certainly much more useful than our hoofs and pasterns. And there's no one like our master when it comes to odd jobs and fixing things, straightening what's twisted and twisting what's straight, and doing all that has to be done without repining or getting downhearted."

Joseph went out and soon returned carrying some straw on his back, wonderful straw, so crisp and glowing that it seemed to herald a miracle.

"What are they preparing there?" said the ass to himself. "It looks like a little bed for a child."

"We may have need of you tonight," said the Virgin to the ox and the ass. The beasts stared at each other for a long time in an effort to understand, and then lay down to sleep.

Soon they were awakened by a voice which, light though it was, had just carried across the whole of heaven. The ox got to his feet, found that there was a naked child asleep in the manger, and methodically warmed him with his breath, all over. The Virgin thanked him with a smiling look. Winged beings came and went, pretending not to see the walls they passed through so easily.

Joseph returned with some swaddling clothes lent him by a neighbor. "It's marvelous," he said in his carpenter's voice, rather loud for such an occasion, "it's midnight, and yet it's day. And there are three suns instead of one. But they're trying to join together."

At dawn the ox got up, taking care where he put his hoofs for fear of waking the child, crushing a heavenly flower, or hurting an angel. How marvelously difficult everything had become!

Neighbors came to see Jesus and the Virgin. They were poor people who had nothing to offer but their beaming faces. After them came others bringing nuts, or a flageolet. The ox and the ass moved aside a little to let them pass, and wondered what impression they themselves would make on the child, who had not yet seen them. He had only just awakened.

"We aren't monsters," said the ass.

"No, but you see we might frighten him with our faces, which aren't at all like his own or his parents'."

"The manger and the stable and its beamed roof haven't got a face like his either, but he isn't afraid of them."

But the ox was not convinced. He thought of his horns and ruminated: "It really is very upsetting not to be able to draw near those you love best without looking threatening. I always have to take care not to hurt anyone, and yet it isn't in my nature to attack people or things without good cause. I'm neither mischievous nor spiteful. But wherever I go, immediately my horns are there with me. I wake up with them, and even when I'm dropping with sleep and shuffle off in a daze, those two hard, pointed things are there and never forget me. I even feel them on the fringe of my dreams in the middle of the night."

A great fear seized the ox and he thought how near he had drawn to the child to warm him. What if he had accidentally gored him! "You oughtn't to go too close to the little one," said the ass, who had guessed his companion's thought. "You mustn't even dream of it, you'd hurt him. Besides, you don't keep your slaver in very well, you might let a drop of it fall on him, and that wouldn't be clean. Thinking of that, why do you slobber like that when you're happy? Keep it to yourself, there's no need to show it to everyone."

(Silence on the part of the ox.)

"For my part, I'm going to offer him my two ears. They twitch, you know, and move in all directions, they haven't any bones and they're soft to touch. They frighten and comfort at the same time. They're just the thing to amuse a child, and at his age they're instructive too."

"Yes, I do know, I've never said the contrary. I'm not a fool."

But since the ass looked really too self-satisfied, the ox added: "But don't you go and bray in his face, or you'd kill him."

"Country bumpkin!" said the ass.

The ass stood on the left of the manger, the ox on the right. These were the positions they occupied at the moment of the Nativity, and the ox, who favored a certain formality, set great store by them. There they remained for hours together, motionless and respectful, as though they were posing for some invisible painter.

Eager for sleep again, the child closed his eyes. Just on the further side of sleep, a shining angel awaited him, to teach him, or perhaps to ask him something. The angel came out of

Jesus' dream and appeared, a living presence, in the stable. After bowing to the newly born, he painted a very pure halo round his head, another for the Virgin, and a third for Joseph. Then off he went in a dazzle of wings and feathers, ever as freshly white and rustling as the whiteness of the tides.

"There's no halo for us," the ox noticed. "The angel's sure to have reasons why not. We're too lowly, the ass and I. Besides, what have we done to deserve such a radiance?"

"You've certainly done nothing, but you forget that I carried the Virgin."

The ox thought to himself: "The Virgin's so beautiful and so fragile, how did she manage to hide this lovely babe?" But perhaps he was thinking aloud, for the ass answered: "There are some things you can't understand."

"Why do you always say that I don't understand? I've had a fuller life than you. I've worked in the mountains, on the plains, and by the sea."

"That isn't the point," said the ass, and went on: "It's not only the halo. I feel sure, ox, that you haven't noticed that all about the child there floats a sort of marvelous dust, or rather it's something better than dust."

"It's much more delicate," said the ox, "it's like a light, a golden mist given off by his little body."

"Yes, but you say that to make people think you'd seen it."

"And hadn't I seen it?"

The ox led the ass to a corner of the stable where, in token of worship, the ruminant had placed a small branch delicately surrounded with wisps of straw, which gave a very good idea of the rays emanating from the divine flesh. It was the first chapel. The ox had brought the straw in from outside. He dared not touch the straw of the manger; he had a superstitious fear of that, because it was good to eat.

The ox and the ass went off to graze until nightfall. Although stones generally take such a long time to understand anything, there were already a good many in the fields which knew. They even came across a pebble which, by a slight change of shape and color, showed them that it was in the secret.

There were meadow flowers, too, which knew and had to be spared. It was quite a business to graze in the fields without committing sacrilege. And to the ox, eating seemed more and more unnecessary. His happiness was food enough.

Before he drank, too, he would ask himself: "And what about this water, does it know?" When in doubt, he preferred not to drink, and would go a little further to some muddy water which was obviously still quite in the dark. Sometimes the only way he could tell was by an infinite sweetness in his throat at the moment when he was swallowing the water. "Too late," the ox would think, "I ought not to have drunk it."

He hardly dared breathe, so sacred and aware did the air seem to him. He was afraid of inhaling an angel.

The ox was ashamed at not always feeling himself as clean as he would have liked. "Well then, I must just be cleaner than before, that's all. It only needs a little more care, and paying attention where I put my feet."

The ass was quite unperturbed.

The sun shone into the stable and the two beasts competed for the honor of shading the child. "I daresay a little sun wouldn't do any harm either," thought the ox, "but the ass is sure to say again that I know nothing about it."

The child went on sleeping and sometimes, in his sleep, he would ponder and frown.

One day, while the Virgin was at the door, answering the thousands of questions put by future Christians, the ass, with his muzzle, delicately turned the child on his side. On going back to her son, Mary had a great fright, as she kept looking for the child's face where she had left it. When she realized what had happened, she gave the ass to understand that it was advisable not to touch the child. The ox showed his agreement by a silence of exceptional quality. He knew how to put rhythm, and shades of meaning, and punctuation, into his dumbness. On cold days you could easily follow the trend of his thoughts by the length of the column of steam that escaped from his nostrils. In that way you could learn a great deal.

The ox thought he had no right to render any but indirect services to the child, such as attracting to himself the flies in the stable (every morning he went and rubbed his back against a hive of wild bees), or squashing insects against the wall. The ass kept a lookout for noises from outside, and when he thought something was suspicious, he barred the entrance. Then the ox would immediately place himself behind the ass, to form a block. They both of them made themselves as heavy as possible: while the danger lasted, their heads and bellies were full of lead. But their eyes shone, more watchful than ever.

The ox was dumfounded to see that, when the Virgin drew near to the manger, she had the gift of making the child smile. And in spite of his beard, Joseph managed it also without too much difficulty, either by his mere presence or by playing on the flageolet. The ox would have liked to play something too. After all, one only had to blow.

"I don't want to say anything against the master, but I don't think he would have been able to warm the Child Jesus with his breath. And as for the flute, all I need is to be alone with the little one, and then he no longer frightens me. He becomes once more a creature who needs protection. And after all, an ox is aware of his strength."

When they were grazing together in the fields, the ox often used to leave the ass.

"Where are you going?"

"I'll be back in a moment."

"But where are you going?" insisted the ass.

"I'm going to see if he needs anything. You never know."

"For goodness' sake leave him alone!"

But the ox went. In the stable there was a kind of round window—such as was later to be called, for that very reason, a bull's eye—through which the ox looked in from outside.

One day he noticed that neither Mary nor Joseph was there. He found the flageolet on a bench, within reach of his muzzle, neither too far away from the child, nor too near to him.

"What shall I be able to play him?" thought the ox, who dared not approach the ear of Jesus except through this musical go-between. "A song of the plow, the war cry of the brave little bull, or the enchanted heifer?"

Oxen often pretend to be ruminating when in their inmost hearts they are singing. The ox blew delicately into the flute and it is not at all certain that an angel did not help him to obtain such pure sounds. The child, on his bed, raised his head and shoulders a little, so as to see. For all that, the flutist was not satisfied with the result. But at least he felt sure that no one outside had heard him. He was mistaken. Then he made off in haste, for fear lest someone, and especially the ass, should come in and catch him too near the little flute.

One day the Virgin said to the ox: "Come and look at my child. You warmed him so well when he was still quite naked; why do you never go near him now?"

Emboldened, the ox placed himself quite close to Jesus who, to put him entirely at ease, seized his muzzle with both hands. The ox held his breath, which had become unnecessary. Jesus smiled. The joy of the ox was a silent joy. It had taken the exact shape of his body and filled it right up to the tips of its horns.

The child looked at the ass and the ox in turn, the ass a little too sure of himself, and the ox who felt himself extraordinarily opaque beside that face so delicately illumined from within, as though one should see, through thin curtains, a lamp passing from one room to another in a very tiny, distant dwelling.

Seeing the ox look so gloomy, the child began to crow with laughter. The animal did not quite understand this laughter, and wondered whether the little one was mocking. Ought he in the future to be more reserved, or even to go away? Then the child laughed again, and his laugh seemed to the ox so luminous, and so filial, that he knew he had been right to stay.

The Virgin and her son often gazed at each other quite close to, and one couldn't tell which was the prouder of the other. "It seems to me that there should be universal rejoicing," thought the ox. "Never has there been seen a purer mother or a more beautiful child. But every now and then how grave they both look!"

The ox and the ass were preparing to return to the stable when the ox, after looking carefully about for fear of making some mistake, said:

"Do look at that star moving across the sky. It's so beautiful it warms my heart."

"Leave your heart out of it, it has nothing to do with the great events we've been witnessing lately."

"You can say what you like, but in my opinion that star is coming in our direction. See how low it is in the sky. It looks as though it's making for our stable. And below it there are three personages covered with precious stones."

The beasts reached the threshold of the stable.

"Well, ox, what is going to happen, according to you?"

"You expect too much of me, ass. I'm content to see what *is* happening, and that's already a good deal."

"I have my own idea."

"Now then, make way," Joseph said to them, opening the door. "Don't you see you're blocking the entrance and preventing these personages from coming in?"

The beasts moved aside to let the Magi pass. There were three of them, one of whom, completely black, represented Africa. At first the ox kept a discreet but watchful eye on him. He wanted to be sure the Negro had none but good intentions toward the new-born. But when the black man, who must have been a little shortsighted, bent down to see Jesus close to, his face, polished and lustrous as a mirror, reflected the image of the child with so much deference, so great a self-forgetfulness, that the heart of the ox was pierced with sweetness because of it.

"It's somebody very distinguished," he thought. "The two others would never have been able to do that." After a few moments he added: "He is indeed the best of the three." The ox had just surprised the white kings at the moment when they were very carefully stowing away in their luggage a wisp of straw, which they had just stolen from the manger. The black king had not wanted to take anything.

The kings slept side by side on an improvised bed lent by some neighbors. "How odd to keep your crown on for sleeping!" thought the ox. "A hard thing like that must be much more uncomfortable than horns. And it must be difficult to get to sleep with all those shining jewels on one's head."

They slept soberly, like statues stretched out on tombs. And their star shone above the manger.

Just before dawn all three got up at the same time, with identical movements. In a dream they had just seen the same angel, who advised them to leave at once and not to go back to the jealous Herod to tell him that they had seen the Child Jesus.

They went out, leaving the star shining above the manger so that everyone should know that that was the place.

The Ox's Prayer

"Celestial Child, please don't judge me by my dazed and obtuse air. May I not one day cease to look like a little lump of rock rolling along?

"As for these horns, I must explain that they are more an ornament than anything else; I'll even admit to you that I've never made use of them.

"Jesus, shed a little of your light on all these imperfections, these confusions that are in me. Teach me a little of your delicacy, you whose tiny feet and hands are attached with such minute care to your body. Can you tell me, little sir, why one day it was enough for me to turn my head to see the whole of you? How I thank you for having been allowed to kneel down before you, marvelous Child, and to live on familiar terms in this way with stars and angels! Sometimes I wonder if you may not have been misinformed, and if I am really the one who ought to be here. Perhaps you haven't noticed that I have a great scar on my back and that some of the hair has been rubbed off my coat on the sides, which is rather unpleasant. Even without going outside my own family, they might have chosen to come here my brother or my cousins who are much better looking than I. Wouldn't the lion or the eagle have been a more suitable choice?"

"Be quiet," said the ass, "why do you keep sighing like that, don't you see you're preventing him sleeping, with all those ruminations of yours?"

"He's right," said the ox to himself, "one ought to know when it's time to be silent, even if one is conscious of a happiness so great that one doesn't know where to put it."

But the ass was praying too!

"Draught asses and pack asses, our path in life is going to be beautiful, and our foals will wait in cheerful pastures to see what happens next. Thanks to you, my little man, stones will remain in their proper places at the side of the road and we shan't have them falling on top of us. And another thing. Why should there still be hills and even mountains in our way? Wouldn't it suit everyone better to have flat country everywhere? And why does the ox, who is stronger than I, never carry anyone on his back? And why are my ears so long, and I've no hair on my tail, and my shoes are so small, and my chest is narrow, and my voice has the color of bad weather? But perhaps these things haven't yet been finally settled?"

During the nights which followed, it was the task now of one star and now of another to be on guard; and sometimes of whole constellations. In order to hide the secret of the sky, a cloud always occupied the place where the absent stars ought to have been, and it was marvelous to see the Infinitely Remote making themselves quite tiny so as to take up their positions over the crib, and keeping their excess of heat and light, and their immensity, for themselves alone, giving off only enough to warm and light the stable, and not to frighten the child. In those first nights of Christianity, the Virgin, Joseph, the Child, the Ox, and the Ass were extraordinarily themselves. During the daytime this likeness to themselves was less noticeable, being scattered about among the visitors; but after sunset it became miraculously concentrated and reliable.

Many animals approached the ox and the ass to ask if they could make the acquaintance of the Child Jesus. And one fine day a horse, known for his friendly disposition and his speed, was chosen by the ox, with Joseph's agreement, to summon the very next day all those who wanted to come.

The ass and the ox wondered whether they ought to let the wild beasts enter, and also the dromedaries, camels, and elephants, all of them animals whose humps and trunks and surplus of flesh and bone render them somewhat suspect.

There was the same doubt about such frightful insects as the scorpions, tarantulas, great trap-door spiders, and vipers who, both male and female, secrete poison in their glands night and day, and even at dawn, when all things are pure.

The Virgin did not hesitate. "You can let them all come in. My child is as safe in his crib as he would be in the topmost heights of heaven."

"And one by one!" added Joseph, in an almost military tone. "I don't want to have two animals at a time passing through the door, or we shan't know where we are."

The poisonous animals were allowed in first, since everyone felt that one owed them this compensation. Particularly noticeable was the tact of the serpents, who avoided looking at the Virgin, gliding by as far away from her person as possible.

And they departed with as much calmness and dignity as if they had been doves or watchdogs.

There were also some animals so small that it was difficult to know if they were there or still waiting outside. These atoms were allowed a whole hour in which to present themselves and make the tour of the crib. When the time was up, although Joseph felt from a slight pricking of his skin that they had not all gone, he ordered the next animals to appear.

The dogs could not help showing their surprise that they had not been allowed to live in the stable like the ox and the ass. Everyone stroked them by way of an answer, whereupon they retired full of visible gratitude.

When it was evident from his smell that the lion was approaching, in spite of everything the ox and the ass were not easy in their minds, and the less so because that smell passed right through the incense and myrrh and other perfumes which the three kings had liberally diffused, without even taking any notice of them. The ox appreciated the generous motives which inspired the confidence of the Virgin and Joseph; but to put such a delicate flame as a child beside a beast whose breath might extinguish it with a single puff . . . !

The anxiety of the ox and the ass was the greater because, as they clearly saw, it was only fitting that they should be totally paralyzed before the lion. They could no more think of attacking him than of thunder or lightning. And the ox, weakened by fasting, felt airy rather than pugnacious.

The lion entered with his mane, which only the wind of the desert had ever combed, and his melancholy eyes which said: "I am the lion, I can't help it, I am only the king of beasts." You could see that his chief concern was to take up as little room as possible in the stable, which was not easy, to breathe without upsetting anything around him, and to forget his retractile claws and the very powerful muscles that moved his jaws. He advanced with lowered lids, hiding his admirable teeth like a shameful disease, and with such a modest bearing that it was quite obvious he belonged to the family of lions who were one day to refuse to devour Saint Blandine. The Virgin took pity and tried to reassure him with a smile like those she kept for her child. The lion gazed straight in front of him, as though to say in a tone still more desperate than a moment ago:

"What have I done that I should be so big and strong? You know well that I've never eaten except when hunger and fresh air compelled me. And you know, too, that I had to consider the cubs. All of us have tried, more or less, to be herbivorous. But grass doesn't suit us; we can't digest it."

Then, in the midst of a great silence which embarrassed everyone, he bent his huge head, like an explosion of hair and fur, and laid it sadly on the hard earth, while the tuft at the end of his tail seemed as overcome as his head.

When it was the tiger's turn, he flattened himself out on the ground until, by sternly humbling himself, he became a veritable bedside mat at the foot of the crib. Then in a moment, with incredible exactitude and elasticity, he reconstituted himself and went out without a word.

The giraffe showed his feet for a moment in the embrasure of the door, and it was unanimously agreed that "that counted" as if he had walked all round the crib.

It was the same with the elephant; all he did was to kneel before the threshold and swing his trunk with a kind of censing movement which was greatly appreciated by all.

A tremendously woolly sheep clamored to be shorn on the spot. They thanked her but did not take her fleece.

The mother kangaroo was desperately eager to give Jesus one of her young, pleading that she really longed to make the present, that it was no sacrifice for her, and that she had other little kangaroos at home. But Joseph took a different view and she had to take her child away.

The ostrich was more fortunate; she took advantage of a moment of inattention to lay her egg in a corner and quietly depart, leaving this souvenir which no one noticed till the next morning. The ass discovered it. He had never seen anything so big or so hard in the way of an egg, and thought it was a miracle. Joseph did his best to undeceive him; he made an omelette of it.

The fish, not having been able to put in an appearance because of their wretched breathing when out of water, had delegated a sea gull to represent them.

The birds departed leaving their songs, the pigeons their loves, the monkeys their tricks, the cats their gaze, and the turtledoves their throaty sweetness.

The animals who have not yet been discovered would have liked to present themselves too, those who await a name in the bosom of the earth or the sea, in depths so great that for them it is always night, without stars or moon or change of seasons.

One could feel, beating in the air, the souls of those who had not been able to come, or were late, and of others who, living at the end of the world, had nevertheless set out on insect feet so small that they could only have gone a yard in an hour, and whose life was so short that they could never hope to cover more than half a yard—and even that only with a good deal of luck.

There were some miracles: the tortoise hurried, the iguana slackened his pace, the hippopotamus was graceful in his genuflections, and the parrots kept silence.

A little before sunset, something happened which upset everyone. Exhausted from having superintended the procession all day, without a bite to eat, in an absent-minded moment Joseph squashed a poisonous spider with his foot, forgetting that it had come to pay its respects to the Child. And the saint looked so upset that everyone felt distressed for quite a long time.

Certain animals who might have been expected to show more discretion lingered in the stable: the ox had to drive out the ferret, the squirrel, and the badger, who did not want to leave.

A few moths remained, taking advantage of the fact that

they were the same color as the beams of the roof to spend the whole night above the crib. But the first sunbeam next day revealed them and, since Joseph did not wish to favor anyone, he turned them out immediately.

Some flies, who were also asked to leave, conveyed by their reluctance to depart that they had always been there, and Joseph did not know what to say to them.

The supernatural apparitions among which the ox lived often took his breath away. Having got into the habit of holding it, as Eastern ascetics do, like them he became a visionary; and although much less at ease among great than among humble things, he experienced genuine ecstasies. But he was governed by a scruple which would not let him imagine angels or saints. He saw them only when they really were in the neighborhood.

"Poor me!" thought the ox, scared by these apparitions, which seemed to him suspect. "Poor me, who am only a beast of burden, or maybe even the devil. Why have I got horns like him, when I've never done evil? And what if I were nothing but a sorcerer?"

Joseph did not fail to notice the anxieties of the ox, who was growing visibly thinner. "Go and eat out of doors!" he cried. "You stay here glued to us all day, soon you'll be nothing but skin and bones."

The ass and the ox went out.

"It's true you're thin," said the ass. "Your bones have become so sharp that you'll have horns sticking out all over your body."

"Don't talk to me of horns!"

And the ox said to himself: "He's quite right, of course, one must live. Go on, then, eat that lovely tuft of green! And what about that other one? What's the matter with you, are you wondering if it's poisonous? No, I'm not hungry. All the same, how beautiful that child is! And those splendid figures who come and go, breathing through their ever-beating wings, all those celestial great ones who find their way into our simple stable without ever getting dirty. Come now, eat, ox, don't trouble your head with all that. And another thing, you mustn't always wake up when happiness tugs at your ears in the middle of the night. And don't stay so long on one knee near the crib that it hurts you. Your hide is all worn away at the knee joint; a bit more and the flies will be at it."

One night it was the turn of the constellation of the Bull to stand guard above the manger, against a stretch of black sky. The red eye of Aldebaran, blazing and magnificent, shone quite close, and the taurine flanks and horns were adorned with huge precious stones. The ox was proud to see the Child so well guarded. Everyone was sleeping peacefully, the ass with his ears trustingly lowered. But the ox, although fortified by the supernatural presence of that constellation which was both a relation and a friend, felt weak all over. He thought of his sacrifices for the Child, of his useless vigils, of the paltry protection he had offered.

"Has the constellation of the Bull seen me?" he wondered. "Does that big starry eye, shining enough to frighten you, know that I'm here? Those stars are so high and far off that one doesn't even know which way they're looking."

Suddenly Joseph, who had been tossing on his bed for the past few moments, got up, raising his arms to heaven. Though as a rule so restrained in words and gestures, he now wakened everyone, even the Child.

"I've seen the Lord in a dream. We must leave without delay. It's because of Herod, he wants to get hold of Jesus."

The Virgin took her son in her arms as though the king of the Jews were already at the door, with a butcher's knife in his hand.

The ass got to his feet.

"And what about him?" said Joseph to the Virgin, pointing to the ox.

"I'm afraid he's too weak to come with us."

The ox wanted to show that it wasn't so. He made a terrific

effort to rise, but never had he felt himself so tethered to the ground. Desperate for help, he looked up at the constellation of the Bull, on which alone he now relied for strength to leave. But the celestial bovine, still in profile to the ox, his eye red and blazing as ever, gave no sign.

"It's several days now since he ate anything," said the Virgin to Joseph.

"Oh, I know very well they're going to leave me here," thought the ox. "It was too good to last. Besides, I should only have been a bony, laggard apparition on the road. All my ribs are tired of my skin and the only thing they want now is to lie down and rest under the open sky."

The ass went up to the ox and rubbed his muzzle against that of the ruminant, to let him know that the Virgin had just recommended him to a neighbor, and that he would lack nothing after their departure. But the ox, his lids half-closed, seemed utterly crushed.

The Virgin stroked him and said: "But we're not going on a journey, of course we aren't. It was only to frighten you!"

"Why of course, we're coming back immediately," added Joseph, "one doesn't set out on a far journey in the middle of the night like this."

"It's a very beautiful night," went on the Virgin, "and we're going to take advantage of it to give the Child some air; he's a bit palish these last days."

"That's absolutely true," said the holy man.

It was a pious lie. The ox knew it and, not wanting to embarrass the travelers in their preparations, he pretended to fall into a deep sleep. That was his way of lying.

"He's fallen asleep," said the Virgin. "Let's put the straw of the crib quite near to him, so that he'll lack nothing when he wakes. And let's leave the flageolet within reach of his breath," she went on in a low voice, "he's very fond of playing it when he's alone."

They got ready to leave. The stable door creaked. "I ought to have oiled it," thought Joseph, who was afraid of wakening the ox. But the ox went on pretending to be asleep. They closed the door carefully.

While the ass of the manger was gradually turning into the ass of the flight into Egypt, the ox remained with his eyes fixed on that straw where a short while before the Infant Jesus lay. Well he knew that he would never touch it, any more than he would touch the flageolet.

The constellation of the Bull regained the zenith with a bound, and with a single toss of his horns settled back in the sky in the place which he would never leave again.

When the neighbor came in, a little after dawn, the ox had ceased to ruminate.

THE FLIGHT INTO EGYPT

The Child had awakened at the moment of departure, when the Virgin, on the ass, took him from Joseph's arms.

"Is he asleep?" the carpenter asked a little later.

"Yes, he is."

"Poor little one, that's the best thing he could have done."

On they went, lighted neither too much nor too little by the moon in its first quarter. Some stars watched them pass, without winking, and an astronomer with his apparatus would have noticed nothing unusual in the whole vault of heaven.

Joseph had been afraid that the Child's head might be surrounded by a halo during the journey, as it was in the crib. Fortunately there was no shining from that quarter. God approved of their moving in the dark. The angels showed themselves surprisingly restrained. There was no question at all of their providing an escort, and if here and there one saw an occasional cloud shaped like an angel, it was so discreetly done that one could not reasonably blame the sky for it.

Dawn lightly brushed the horizon. There was nobody on the road, nothing but a poor desiccated palm tree. "So much the better," said Joseph. "I distrust chatterboxes, even when they mean well."

As they passed before the tree, it bent its one and only knee and prostrated itself in the dust. At this gesture the Child, who had just been awakened by the first ray of sunlight, began to laugh; and the Virgin found the scene very pretty.

"But it's terribly dangerous!" cried Joseph, in a voice which he tried in vain to muffle. "If the trees begin to bow to us, I give Herod less than two hours to find us."

"God is protecting us," said the Virgin. "The absence of the halo proves it."

"I know he's protecting us. All the same, these half-witted trees oughtn't to call everyone's attention to us."

On the horizon, close to a big market town, there was quite a little wood which considerably worried the head of the family. Would those trees be sensible enough to stay in their places, or were they going to leave them suddenly and display an admiration which might prove fatal? As soon as they drew level with this grove, the Child began to look at the palm trees with a shade of malice, as though challenging them to imitate their religious comrade.

"Hide the Child in your cloak," grumbled Joseph.

But Mary, who had no misgivings, did nothing of the kind. Not a tree budged. All that happened was that three doves, whose excessive whiteness made them suspect, accompanied the Holy Family for a short distance.

"One's mind is never at rest," thought Joseph. "If there'd been a mischief-maker about, it would have been all up with the Child."

Meanwhile, they were massacring the Innocents wholesale, hoping against hope that Jesus would be among them. Herod's emissaries entered the houses in two and threes, taking with them certain very cruel children whose instructions were to ferret out those of their own age. After a visit apparently without significance, they would kill your son on the spot as if he were a mere viper. And off they would go, with a look which seemed to expect some kind of horrid thanks. One of Herod's sons, out at nurse in Bethlehem, was also assassinated in obedience to his father's orders.

Once the executioners had become known, it was not long before they began to arrive disguised as beggars or shepherds, traders or charitable ladies.

Everything that might betray the presence of children in a house—toys, little garments, slippers—was carefully hidden. To leave the least of these things lying about was tantamount to: "Please kill my child immediately". And the neighbors were quite right to say: "Aren't you ashamed, assassins?" to careless parents who left a wooden horse or a little trumpet at their door. In order to deceive the authorities, mothers often dressed their children in men's clothes. One even saw milksops of sixteen sticking on false beards, and young girls, whose bosoms were sufficiently obvious, using contrivances to make them look bigger, although no one in his senses would have dreamt of taking them for children.

Day and night the massacring went on. And it was pitiful to see this very young human blood spilt with unheard-of violence, leaving the little bodies of a sudden bereft of both plans and memories, as a result of horrible wounds ten times too big for a child.

All this the Virgin and Joseph knew. No one talked of anything else on the roads of Judaea, where every youthful creature attracted as much attention as a highway bandit. So Joseph made haste to reach Egypt by bypaths.

In the meantime, almost immediately after the Child had gone, the soul of the ox of the manger got out through the dormer window of the stable, not wanting to go through the big door which had let the Family depart.

Once outside he said to himself: "I no longer have either head or hoofs, I am the soul of the ox I was." And shortly afterward: "I'm like a breeze in the sky. No more need to graze or sleep." As a matter of fact, he didn't yet know what to do with all this marvelous lightness.

Not being subject to the resistance of the air, souls can move much more quickly than bodies. That of the ox did not take long to find the Virgin, Joseph, and the Child on the road, still saddened by the state of the creature they had had to leave behind in the stable. "There they are," said the ox joyfully to himself. "It's them all right, with their familiar limbs in their proper places. Oh, how nice they look on the road, just as they always were, not any smaller and not any bigger. To have seen that makes up for all my suffering."

And he went from one to the other, counting them and addressing them familiarly in his very silent way.

But however anxious you are not to put yourself forward, there does all the same come a moment when you want people to know you exist, and that you can see and hear. Circling round the ass, he thought: "We both know each other so well it's absolutely impossible that he shouldn't recognize me." But the ass noticed nothing bovine around him, so the ox perched on the little one's shoulder, like the lightest of birds. He was nothing but air and found himself unprovided with even the flimsiest argument.

"All the same," said the Virgin to Joseph, "I can't get over having left that creature in such a weak state in the stable." Perhaps, thought the ox, this may be the beginning of a conversation which will end in their discovering me. But the Virgin went on: "By this time the poor beast is certainly dead, dead as a doornail. Unless perhaps such a charitable creature has a soul too."

"Don't say silly things, my poor woman," said Joseph, adding immediately, so swiftly do saints repent: "Sorry for 'silly things.' "

"And for 'poor woman,' " added the Virgin.

From time to time the Infant Jesus turned round as if he were looking along the road for the ox, when all that remained of it was in front of him. And the ox said to himself: "Shall I never be able to make them understand I'm here? Well, perhaps it's better that way. The dead are one thing and the living another. A dead person ought to know how to keep his place with dignity and not always be trying to leave it. I must help them to forget me. I daresay that to efface oneself is the best way of showing courtesy and charity. The trouble, when you're nothing but a soul, is that you can't be sure of staying in the same place. Always at the mercy of a puff of wind or a clap of thunder, in this country where storms are so frequent. I suppose I'm indestructible now, but I'm so light that the lightest breath from the travelers blows me aimlessly all over the place, and when the ass gave a sniff a moment ago, he nearly drew me up his nostrils." It was indeed understandable that the ox who, like all those of his tribe, had always been in favor of weighing things carefully, and even of weight in itself, should feel distressed by this disturbing coming and going.

Meanwhile the Virgin, who had been upset by the sudden departure from Bethlehem, was unable to feed the Child as she would have liked. Jesus did not cry, of course, but it was easy to see that he was sucking his thumb in secret. And to ask for milk at a farm was highly dangerous, as that would immediately have encouraged people to hunt among your baggage for your child.

The ox rushed from one traveler to the other in his efforts to help. He had suffered so much when he was alive at not being able to do anything really useful for the little one, and here it was beginning all over again now he was dead.

While he was roaming about the countryside, without losing sight of the travelers, he saw a little cow whose curious antics attracted his attention from a distance. He went up to her, thinking to himself that perhaps a member of his own race would understand him better, and found himself saying in the stranger's ear: "Little cow, will you help me to find a small shelter? Make a little room for me under your skin, I won't hurt you." And he was dumfounded to hear the cow answer: "But whoever are you?"

"I am the lost soul of an ox."

"And why do you pick on me to make room for you under my skin? I'd have you know, ox, that I myself take up all the room there is. My skin is a covering solely for my own use that I wouldn't lend to my best friend."

"You wouldn't even notice my presence. And besides you might need somebody. One is sometimes very lonely in one's skin."

"No, no, that's all just a lost soul's yarn. Get along with you, ox, I don't even know you."

The cow was beginning to give in. The ox thought to himself that an attempt might be made through her nostrils. Taking advantage of a moment when she was breathing in, he found his way without more ado into the head of the female ruminant.

"Oh, I know very well that you're inside me now," said the cow. "But I warn you that if you inconvenience me in any way, I shall drive you out immediately."

"That may not be so easy," thought the bovine soul, in an aside. (But was an aside any longer possible?) "I am only a spirit clothed in flesh which does not belong to me. Well, we shall see."

The ox at once set to work to try and influence the body of this simple-minded, rather silly cow, attempting to control and reason with her for the benefit of all concerned. As he never quitted the heart and brain of his hostess for a moment, it did not take long to persuade her that it was absolutely necessary to gallop across country to catch up with his former masters.

"Don't turn round," said Joseph to the Virgin. "Someone's following us."

Joseph turned round himself out of a sense of duty. And the cow at once came to a halt beside the Child, pointing with her horns to her udders swollen with milk.

"You can milk that fine little cow," said the Virgin.

"But she'll give us away with these unusual attentions!"

"See, here's a bowl, my little one's hungry," was all the Virgin answered.

Full of suspicion and hiding under a cloak, Joseph made a great business of milking the cow and tasting the milk, as if it were some outlandish medicine. So the Virgin took the bowl from his hands, swallowed two mouthfuls, declared there was nothing diabolic about the liquid, and gave it to the Child, who looked elsewhere to show he wasn't in a hurry. But it was clear from Joseph's looks that he was full of anxiety at the thought of this suspect milk passing through the mouth and the little person of the Child.

"Everything seems natural to you," he said to the Virgin, rather crossly. "If a hundred cows were to offer us their udders, you'd think that was good too."

"There aren't a hundred, there's only one."

"Quite so, Mary, I know how to count. But I can't help wondering whether it's wise for us to accept the services of this creature, even if it's proved she's quite dependable. Just think for a moment of all the animals who came to pay their respects to the Child after his birth. What if the ostrich and the giraffe and the lion and all the others began to follow us! What a clue for Herod's police!"

The Child was now gazing at the cow in an unusually friendly way. "Don't look in that direction," said Joseph, as though they had been in the presence of the devil himself, with four hoofs and a cow's muzzle.

"Poor innocent, why shouldn't he look at her?"

And Jesus began to laugh with happiness when he saw that the cow was coming up to him and that he could touch her muzzle as he used to with the ox in the manger. For him, indeed, the ox and the cow were one and the same beast. What a wonderful power of confusion in the Child, which allowed him to see so clearly!

"One day," said Joseph, his equanimity at last restored, "we'll explain to him what a vast difference there is between a genuine martyr, like the ox, and an animal which may mean well but lacks true greatness."

Meanwhile the Virgin too had begun to pat the good little milker. From then on the cow joined the expedition. But in spite of the ox's admonitions, she sometimes got fidgety when she was being milked. One day Joseph, irritated by this impatience of hers, hid himself from everyone so as not to give a bad example, and delivered a great kick to the empty air, as saints do when they feel dissatisfied (and don't want to commit a sin). And the soul of the ox thought: "Good Joseph, how upset you would be if you knew that I saw you giving that kick."

The ass, who had never liked cows—he found them restless, muddle-headed, and really too conceited about their udders—found himself living happily in the company of this one. It was not so much friendship as the willing acceptance of an enforced proximity. Since his separation from the ox, he no longer felt the need to communicate with other animals. He was like a man who has decided to smoke his pipe in silence for the remainder of his days, drawing from it little puffs so nearly invisible that they seem to come from the soul rather than the body.

The journey continued without harm to the Child. Joseph had ended by considering the presence of the attendant cow a genuine miracle, and even by recognizing that she had rendered many more services to all three of them than had the ox, though this of course in no way diminished in his eyes the rare merits of the creature they had abandoned in the stable.

Never had the ox found himself as much at home in his own skin as in that of the cow: his present usefulness had even cured him of a modesty that was almost morbid. Although he regretted none of his past services, he considered now that he might have made them more useful. He went so far as to think that, instead of letting himself die of grief, he would have done better, while he still had the strength, to have gone in great secrecy to Jerusalem and there to have gored Herod during one of his morning walks. But just how far was that the ox's own idea? Had it not been suggested to him by his companion under the skin?

In the meantime the Romans were requisitioning the livestock on the roads and Joseph was asked where he had got that cow from. Not wanting to lie, he said, blushing: "She began to follow us and to offer us her udders of her own accord." They were all threatened with prison unless he gave a more reasonable reply. Fortunately, the Virgin and her look of profound innocence caused the arms of the soldiers, who had formed a circle round them, to fall to the ground.

"They're feeble-minded," the Roman officer finally said. "We'll take the cow all the same and let them go on their way."

They gave the cow a blow and turned her northward by means of a cord attached to her neck and kicks aimed at every part of her body. The soul of the ox tried in vain to escape from the friendly body so as to stay near the Child. He was henceforth in truth one with her, and felt himself imprisoned in her flesh like a fly in amber. All he could do was to urge the cow to turn her head several times in the direction of the little one, while at the same time he tried his best to share the sufferings of the ill-treated beast.

Joseph and the Virgin walked on for a few days more in anxiety, and then the haloes returned quite naturally to crown their heads—and that of the Child—and make them understand that they no longer had anything to fear. Besides, no one on the road talked any more about the massacre of the Innocents, and among the travelers whom they met, the Egyptian type became more and more pronounced.

THE MAN WHO STOLE CHILDREN

A Novel

translated by Alan Pryce-Jones

PART ONE

I

Antoine was seven, or perhaps eight. He was coming out of a big store, dressed from head to foot in new clothes, as if to face a new life. But for the moment he was still a child with his hand in his nanny's, standing on the pavement of the Boulevard Haussmann.

He was not tall, and in front of him he saw nothing but men's legs and flurried skirts. In the roadway there were hundreds of turning wheels, or wheels which stopped at the feet of a policeman rugged as a rock.

Before crossing the rue du Havre, he noticed, at a newspaper kiosk, a huge footballer's foot kicking the ball heaven knows where. While he was looking eagerly at this picture Antoine had the feeling that someone was pulling him violently away from his nanny. A large hand wearing a black and gold ring had brushed against his ear.

He was carried into a swirl of passers-by. A violet skirt, a pair of striped trousers, a cassock, a laborer's muddy legs, and on the ground a patch of wet soil ruffled by thousands of feet—that is all he saw. Cut off from his nanny, he felt his face reddening. Was it anger at having to acknowledge his powerlessness in the crowd, or a hidden pride crowding for the first time to his cheeks? He lifted his head. The faces round him reflected indifference or tragedy. A few scraps of speech reached him, totally disconnected (it is things such as these which cause the nostalgia of the streets). Amidst the noise, he thought he heard the pitiful cry of his nanny, "Antoine!" Her voice reached him in tatters, as if torn by invisible brambles. It seemed to come from over his shoulder. He retraced his steps, but without replying. And all the time from the street rose a confused noise, the noise which vainly seeks its unity in the clash of a thousand different aspirations. Antoine found it mortifying to have lost his nanny, and did not wish the passers-by to realize what had happened. He was determined to find her by himself. He was walking now along the rue de Provence, and in his palm he could still feel the pressure of a rough and friendly hand, the hardness of which seemed made the better to hold the light fingers of a child.

For five minutes now he had been alone with a kind of shame or anxiety, he could not say which. Night was falling. Paris began to close round him. On his right there stood an automatic clock. Had he even been able to tell the time by it he would have felt less alone. But the white clock face with its two hands persisted in telling him nothing, in pursuing an idea of its own to which he must remain a stranger. Nobody seemed interested in him, and he began to enjoy the fact. He awaited calmly the moment when some gentleman, some lady, some laborer, or postman, or policeman, or someone vaguely composed of all these people, and perhaps also of the cars and bicycles and the horses riding by, would stop in front of him and ask:

"What are you doing in the street, all by yourself, in your new suit?"

But nothing happened. The passers-by walked past him with such indifference that he would have liked to poke their eyes out.

He turned round, and saw behind him a gentleman tall and mild and grave who was watching him with a look of extraordinary kindness. Antoine was not at all surprised to see him. Two or three times in the last few minutes he thought he had caught a glimpse of him watching intently but secretly, as if the unknown gentleman had been on the point of taking a step which he thought extremely important, of linking, in some obscure way, his own life to that of Antoine.

An arc lamp now cast its light full upon the man's face. He was wearing a thin mustache, very black and drooping, and in his eyes was something of the fan-shaped glance of the paterfamilias standing with his quiverful spread before him.

There was an odd stab in Antoine's heart.

It was the recollection of his nanny preparing to leave him, and then disappearing. Antoine was hooked, stolen away by an adventure from which he felt it impossible to escape, and he was in no way surprised when the man with the mustache bent double in order to reach down to his own level:

"Antoine Charnelet, my boy," said he in a voice which trembled with emotion, "so you have lost your nanny. Don't be frightened. We are already friends, and you shall see that we have met before."

The tall man had a slight accent.

"Will you get into my car?"

It was a magnificent car, so new that it seemed still to be standing in a shop window in the Champs-Elysées.

"Will you come home with me until we find your nanny again?" And he looked so natural in his intense simplicity that Antoine was not surprised to find himself jumping into the car without so much as answering. The man spoke a few words in a foreign language to his chauffeur, who was a Negro of the utmost politeness.

Hardly had he sat back when Antoine began to remember the toys which an unknown donor had been sending him regularly for some time past. They had been really magnificent toys, but there was never the least indication of who had sent them.

For instance, in a huge box, there had been a South American farm, a herd of cows wandering about the country. They were sniffing an unfamiliar air and seemed to find themselves in Paris by accident. The eucalyptus trees, if you set them out on the carpet, cast about them the shadow of immense distances.

Gauchos were cantering in these imaginary deserts and throwing their lassos. A horse fell, a spell cast about its hooves.

Another box contained a coffee plantation. Pipe in mouth, one watched the settlers passing in the heat of the day. The untrodden forests were reflected in their eyes. Some of them stopped for an instant as if they had forgotten something. And sure enough, a dog leaped toward them, with a parcel in its mouth.

But here we are, getting close to the coffee trees. They stand there in wide straight lines to infinity. How can we enter? Do as the settlers do.

There had also been a cigar-box. On the bands you could read, *Rio*. You only had to set a match to the end in order to see the bay in all its splendor, the ships at anchor, the mountains round and above the city, the flawless sky.

Antoine, who had hitherto had nothing but an occasional cheap present from his nanny, was confounded by the arrival of these treasures.

At home, aloud and in undertones, all kinds of guesses were made. Who had sent them?

Just as he was thinking of the cigars still lying side by side in their box, Antoine recognized on his companion's finger the black and gold ring of the man who had seemed to separate him from Rose. He hesitated whether to shout out of the window.

"Go on as you are going, straight on!"

Beside the stranger Antoine felt himself in so comforting a province of calm that he knew no fear. But he wondered why he had been snatched away from Rose.

He kept his confidence. The gentleman smelt good (a discreet smell of cleanliness mixed with a touch of eau de Cologne). And he appeared respectable, infinitely starred with respectability, like night falling upon the earth. Antoine felt that he was traveling toward a shadowy threshold beyond which the sun would be shining.

"Is this what you like, my boy? I want you to be happy," said the man out of the depths of a vast anxiety, and as ill at ease as if he had revealed a secret.

Antoine twiddled the buttons of his overcoat, and stuffed his hands into the pockets of his new suit.

The car stopped in front of a building in the Square Laborde. There was a lift like the lift at home. The stranger made him get carefully into it and between two floors asked him how he felt. They were at the third floor landing when Antoine replied that he felt quite all right. After another floor and a half of thought the stranger added:

"You won't be bored in my house; there are other children, and they are waiting for you."

At the noise of the lift, several children opened the door and came out to greet the stranger, whose name was Colonel Philemon Bigua. They looked happy enough—little faces at different heights. The biggest held a football in his hand. All of them stared at the new arrival with extreme curiosity, as if they had many things to teach him. Antoine's memory worked at full stretch. He seemed to hear it inside his head. Forgetfulness fled away in all directions as though never to return.

"Here is someone for you to play with," said the stranger.

A fifteen-year-old hand was stretched out to Antoine, and then two others smaller than his own.

II

Colonel Philemon Bigua introduced Antoine to his wife in the most offhand way.

"This is the little Charnelet."

Desposoria was plump and handsome, and her eyes were always turned in splendor toward her husband. In the look which passed between them there was a sensation of good work well done.

A nurse washed Antoine's hands and face in the presence of his new friends; they did not leave him and watched him with avidity. They had understood where he came from and how uncomfortable he must have felt.

Meantime, the Colonel and his wife went off, whispering to one another, toward a room which Antoine had not yet seen. His hands were washed, his hair brushed. One of his friends pinched his arm, another gave him a friendly kick with the point of his red slipper. Soon they all sat down to dinner. Antoine was delighted to have eyes more or less of his own age, and at his own height, in front of him. He had never had a meal except with his nanny, who was affectionate but usually sat sideways; he saw her as though at the bottom of a crystal ball bearing her flowerlike name, Rose. In the same ball, but with their backs turned, he saw first his mother, with a hat on her head, saying good-bye without looking at him, her hand already on the door handle; then, making a brief appearance, there were his mother's friends: an old lady, a young lady, a rosy, clean-shaven young man, whose politeness was positively angelic, and who might or might not have been wearing a mustache. And for the last month, once a week, there had been those toys dropped out of the blue.

In the Colonel's house, Antoine found each object astonishing. The tablecloth, the glasses, the shining glances, new and clean. The dishes were wonderful, so were the plates under the filtered light. The hour was important, the table large, and he was impressed by so many *lively* faces sitting round it. He observed the mouthfuls which slip between the lips and then disappear forever. On the table, the bread, even the crumbs, astonished him, and so did the water in big glasses like the water in a fairy story.

He sat on the Colonel's right hand. The Colonel cut up

his meat for him and kept explaining it, as well as the gravy, the fat, the bread, everything which was on the table and had no need of explanation. The Colonel built up his reputation discreetly by refusing wine, eating little, proffering the best pieces, buttering slices of bread, saying no to apple fool. But after it was all over, what should he do but take up an enormous cup of coffee, three times the size of the others, and drink it without sugar and without taking his eyes off Antoine?

Bigua took the little boy into the drawing room, motioned his wife to leave the room, and after a short pause (it was as if his heart, in its anxiety, were growing pale in his breast) he said:

"If you like, Antoine, I'll take you home at once."

The little boy said nothing, feeling that the whole matter was no business of his—it was a thing to be settled by the grownups.

"Or would you rather stay with us?"

Antoine underlined with a fresh silence the silence which already reigned.

"Very well, then, go and play, and if ever you want to go home, come and tell me, and I'll take you back at once."

The little boy went back to his friends in the playroom. He was pushed into a far corner.

"Where were you stolen?" they asked him.

"In front of the Galeries Lafayette."

"All of us have been stolen."

The word "stolen" nearly put Antoine into a temper, but the other children used it with the respectable air that a nobleman might assume in speaking of the nobility, or an academician in referring to *mes confrères de l'Académie*.

"As for me," said Fred, "I was stolen in London, in a fog."

"So was I," said his brother, "we were hand in hand."

Antoine saw that they were twins and noticed that they spoke with a slight English accent.

"And I was in bed," said the eldest of the children.

"Don't stay there doing nothing," ordered Desposoria, coming into the room. "Run about, amuse yourselves, and then you shall go to bed."

"Yes, mamma," said three voices on the special note which covers a lie.

The children began to run about aimlessly while Desposoria watched them, and Antoine could get no further information on his friends.

He was put to bed by the Colonel and his wife, who on that first evening did not want to hand him over to the nurse. The man took a tape measure out of his pocket and carefully took Antoine's measurements, which he then dictated to Desposoria.

Lightly, but with some disquietude, the Colonel prodded the little boy's body as if to make sure that no rupture, no suspicious lump were there. He turned back gently one of his eyelids; it was fine and red, and the child seemed healthy enough. The Colonel gave his wife an almost imperceptible sign of satisfaction. Antoine was put to bed, the two heads, so utterly unknown, leaned over his pillow, the Colonel held out his hand, Desposoria kissed him tenderly and told him pleasant things in a language which he could not understand.

The Colonel went out, followed by his wife. Her curiosity showed in her face, but he stopped her with a gesture and said, with a mysterious pinch of the lips, "No, my dear, I shan't tell you anything tonight. I want to be alone."

Then, "You mustn't mind." And he kissed her on the forehead as he might have kissed an elder daughter.

Calmly, Desposoria left the room. There was no expression on her face.

The Colonel had a room of his own. He needed space for his legs and for his long arms and for his ideas which spilled all over the place.

He sank deeply into an armchair and began to think out loud:

"His house was warmed and hung with mirrors, and he was a lost child just the same . . ."

It seemed to Antoine that these faces which had newly come into his life were cut off from him by a long, long tunnel. He went off to sleep in clean sheets, but his inner spirit still refused to be put to bed. It stayed outside the blankets. An hour later, it woke him, as if it were afraid of solitude. But Antoine was not sure what had broken his sleep, nor even precisely where he was. He threw out one arm, expecting to find a familiar wall, and the exact roughness of the paper in his own room; and so great was the gulf before him that he nearly fell out of bed. He could distinctly hear the voice of that inner spirit:

"Why did you consent to follow that man in the street? What are you doing all alone in this house among people whom you did not even know this morning? Have you done what you should, Antoine Charnelet?"

Antoine saw his mother coming into the room. She looked at him as she had never done before, with feverish attention—the attention which is kept for victims of an accident before the blood has been wiped from their faces. She sat on the edge of the bed, her eyes turned toward him with amazement. She kept silence as if she had totally unlearned the art of speech. Her eyes were so deeply blue that one could not imagine any living person possessing anything like them; it seemed as if only the spotless dead could show such a blue. To set the gentleness of her face in its full relief, she looked at her son, or rather gave him nothing but her eyes to look at. She was a new mother, shaped by skilled hands which had taken care that nothing maternal should be omitted. She was wearing a miraculous gray kimono in which from time to time Antoine caught the reflection of a falling star.

She crossed her hands on her knees as when there is nothing more to be said in a sick room—only the nightlight to be lit.

Antoine's mother showed no surprise at seeing him in an unknown room. She had surrendered the art of speaking, of explaining, to her face, to her hands, to her delicate cheeks, to her dress, to the bows on her pretty shoes. The hat she was wearing, in spite of the kimono, with an extraordinary naturalness—carried an ornament, and a dark veil which fell over her shoulders. But now she was moving about, opening a basket which she had hitherto kept hidden, and pulling from it a handful of shining objects which served no apparent purpose, but with which she began to play. For a minute or two she played very seriously, frowning all the time as if her living depended on it. Then she turned toward Antoine a face in which shone six brilliant tears, motionless, crystalline. He wondered what it was she wanted—this mother of his whose power of seduction seemed to renew itself almost invisibly under his very eyes like the water of a waterfall against the dark background of a forest?

Antoine dared not open his mouth. Words crept from his heart into his throat and dropped back again immediately.

The vision disappeared.

There was nothing now before his eyes except the night air, the air of the Square Laborde, imprisoned in his room. Through the open window he could see the stars which twinkled upon that part of the city. With beating heart he longed to get dressed, to run toward his mother so as to find out whether she was thinking about him as much *as she pretended.*

The seconds passed. Antoine now imagined that his mother and Rose were waiting for him at the door of his own home. One of them was looking one way along the street, the other stood in tears, and each time a taxi passed they followed it with their eyes until they could no longer see its number, nor its lights.

With what eagerness he began to dress in order to go home! It seemed to him that the Colonel's person, his stately presence, were only a fleeting vision in the life of Antoine Charnelet. It was hard to get his shoes on, and his socks got caught into a lump at the heel. How could he tie his laces? He hesitated, he saw the Colonel's face once again. Why must he be the one to be chosen out of all the little boys in the street, and what did the intruder want with him?

Antoine buttoned his overcoat carefully on top of clothes which were put on anyhow. Where was his hat? Hanging on a hook. It was out of reach. Should he push a chair under it? He was afraid of making a noise; he didn't need a hat. He got to the door of his room; then there was the room of the nurse to cross. There was a slight sigh as she half woke, and a second later he was in the hall. It was dark, and he could feel that he was walking on his shoelaces.

Now he was on the staircase, and sitting in turn on each of the steps he slid gently down in the shadows. Happiness was struggling within him. There he was, in the trousers which he had to hold up in his hand, carrying his seven years toward the big glass door which gave on to the square. It had black bars, rather like the door in his own home. Already he saw the grave light of the street, and with the light of the tall lamps he knew one must not trifle.

"Door, please."

He walked out. He had to go home. In a confused way he told his legs that much, and asked them for the secret: how did one get to the Parc Monceau? Then he asked a man who was tapping his stick carefully along.

"You're out of luck, young man; I'm blind."

He asked a newspaper-seller who put him on the right road. He ran as fast as he could, as though he had only a hundred yards to go. But almost immediately it seemed to him as though his journey would last until the very end of his life.

As he ran, he thought he could hear the murmuring of the buildings. When they saw a child alone in the street at this hour they made comments on so odd an event.

At last he reached home. There stood the house, five stories high. There was no light on the third floor. Could his mother be asleep, then? He was stupefied to see her neither on the balcony nor on the pavement. Rose was not there either. He had been completely forgotten, on a night like this! The *porte cochère* of the house, chilly and mute, made no allusion to what had happened. It looked at Antoine without recognizing him, as if he had completely changed.

He looked toward the ground, perhaps to find a decision there. And suddenly, on the pavement, he found his tortoise, a small tortoise which he had been taking care of. Dead? He took it up in his arms; it was alive; its little head, its four legs were moving. Perhaps it had fallen from the balcony where he had arranged a box for it; perhaps it had wandered off in search of him. There was nothing the matter with it, anyway.

Antoine stood there, with the tortoise in his hand. He would show it to his new friends. He walked slowly back, and then quicker and quicker, to the Square Laborde. He met nothing on his way except the trees beside the street—those trees which even in the heart of a city offer the signs and tokens of universal resignation.

Through the mists of sleep which began to wrap his whole body, Antoine wondered how he would get back into the Colonel's house without a key. He crawled up the stairs after pressing the button which would keep the electric light alight for just two minutes. He decided to sit on the landing, with his back against the door until a more favorable moment. But the door opened behind him at the very moment that the light went out.

No. There was no stately presence, no Colonel's wife, nobody, behind the door. He had accidentally taken his precautions, and left the door unlatched.

Antoine and his sleepiness were back again in the Colonel's house. Both of them, they crossed the nurse's room, and heard her say in a muffled voice from under the bedclothes:

"You must keep better hours, Antoine. It isn't natural to have to get up in the middle of the night."

"Oh, it was *exceptional*," Antoine answered, using that word for the first time in his life.

And he clutched his tortoise under that coat of his which seemed really to conceal everything which was exceptional in the world.

III

Meantime the Colonel, in the next room, was not asleep. But his mind was working too sharply for him to be able to hear what was going on on the other side of the door.

He saw himself once again wandering round the London Zoo. He loved wild beasts, and he loved elephants, which are huge children dressed in the most solid of skins.

It was on a winter's day, and he had just been reading a notice which left him deep in thought:

> Lost children should be
> Applied for at the
> Ladies' Waiting Room
> By the Eastern Aviary
> Near the Clock Tower.

"So there are people who have such a lot of children that they lose them, and then there is a whole organization to collect them and give them back!"

All of a sudden, he saw a pair of beggars nearing a bench in the fog. The man and the woman each held a child by the hand: twins, one would have said, and about four years old. While the parents seemed dressed in rags and tatters, the children were got up with an elegance which was almost touching.

The couple sat them down on the bench. Under her skirt—which was the color of waste ground—the mother carried a kind of bag, and from it she pulled two pieces of chocolate wrapped in silver paper. She gave one to each of the children with a movement so grave and intense that these single mouthfuls might have been meant to nourish them all the days of their life.

"Eat this and be quiet."

And with hasty steps the parents made off into the fog.

For a long time Bigua walked up and down. It seemed to him that he had a responsibility for the two children. He was the one person to have seen the beggars leave them on the bench. But did they really mean to leave them?

He remembered the notice:

Lost children should be . . .

"It would be horribly cruel to give the children back to their parents. And anyway could one ever find them? Supposing they have gone to throw themselves into the Thames?"

Bigua walked once more all round the bench. The fog became thicker. One of the children had fallen asleep. At that the Colonel hesitated no longer, and he led them away toward the exit, leaving the Clock Tower on the left. The collar of his fur-lined coat and his air of splendor drove a narrow channel through the fog on either hand. Back at his hotel, he found in the pockets of the children a piece of paper on which was written:

"Be good to us. We are twin brothers and orphans, four years old, born in Staffordshire."

My name is Fred, said one piece of paper.

My name is Jack, said the other.

That very evening, Bigua went back to Paris with his wife and the twins.

Next the Colonel began to think about Joseph, the big boy of fifteen whom we saw just now in the hall, with a football in his hand. He had been stolen in Paris . . . But it is not yet the right moment to talk about him.

"Four of them!" exclaimed the Colonel. His nostrils were set wide apart. "When I look at this bare arm"—for he was in the act of undressing—"I cannot avoid the fact that it belongs to a kidnapper!"

There was a magnifying glass on his table.

"If I examine my arm under the microscope, there is the skin and there are the hairs of a kidnapper, and there is a thief's nose magnified twelve times," he went on, walking up to the looking glass which hung above the fireplace. "Ah well, good night, off to bed we go! But first I'll just make sure that the last child has everything he wants, that he's still alive."

He turned the switch in the next room. Antoine had just come in and was pretending to be asleep. Delicately his almost imperceptible breathing stirred the sheets. But it was enough to reassure an anxious Colonel, seven thousand sea miles away from home, standing with bare feet on a thick carpet.

Before going back to his own room, the Colonel mechanically folded the child's things, which Antoine, after his expedition, had chucked down on various pieces of furniture. Philemon Bigua was not surprised by this chaos; his thoughts were elsewhere. He did not notice that Antoine's shoes were covered in fresh mud and that there were mud stains on his overcoat—all over it, in fact.

The next morning, Bigua, walking through the drawing room, noticed something on the carpet. Could it be a tortoise? Tortoise, how have you managed to creep into this respectable house?

Antoine insisted on being given the tortoise, and given it he was.

For a long time the Colonel wondered where the tortoise had come from. He felt that there was something odd about its arrival in his house, and that the matter contained a mystery to be cherished, not unveiled. Several times a day he went toward the tortoise with the utmost secrecy, took it in his hands, turned it this way and that, examining with scrupulous care the claw, the tiny head, the knotted shell. He wanted to put it on the balcony, but Antoine put up so violent a protest that he left it in his room.

At night, Antoine put the tortoise into his bed. He could not get off to sleep. In the next room, he could hear the steps of the austere and vigorous foreigner who had borne down upon him in the street, with ears pricked, to carry him off. At that very moment, Bigua coughed, not because he had a cold, but so as to remind Antoine that he was there quite close to him, with his throat and his larynx as large as life.

Painfully Antoine drowsed off. He woke up again before long, in the grip of a nightmare: he had seen his mother holding out to him her white arms, but her hands, and her ring, belonged to Philemon Bigua.

Antoine jumped out of his nightmare. In his nightshirt, he rushed to take refuge in the arms of reality, in the depths of the Colonel's room. The Colonel kissed, calmed him, put him to bed, fetched him a drink. Antoine looked at the hands of his ravisher: hands of a different stock, born under far-off skies and long strengthened by the milk of wild herds.

"Would you like me to take you home this very minute?"

"No."

"Tomorrow morning?"

"Never."

Bigua hugged Antoine in his arms, with a vigor and gratitude which disgusted the child.

IV

A young woman in a room. She had just come in. It was eight o'clock by her little watch made of dark blue enamel. It was easy to tell by her air that she knew nothing of what had happened. Who was she and where did she come from? She stood there like someone on the screen when the film is half over and one has only just walked into the darkness of the cinema. But the image, before one's eyes, is already in the present indicative.

What then does she want with us? One thing alone is certain: she is beautiful and restless, in this room lit with a hard light. Small, rather fair, with long shining eyes—vague eyes which try to rest upon several objects at once. . . . She went toward her desk and wrote in a hurry on a little pile of visiting cards.

All at once she thought of something, and stopped. Ah yes, her child. The thought of the child floated down to her from the outside world. (It was not carried on the flood of previous imaginings.) She opened and shut her blotter with a nervous gesture, and displayed in one corner of it the name HÉLÈNE written in silver, in small capital letters.

A long train of thought bore her away as the fancy struck her. Yet she managed to write quickly on their envelopes the names of three guests, two ladies and a gentleman.

There are two letters for the *seizième arrondissement,* and one for the *quatrième,* she thought with a false lucidity, and that's that. Behind her, on the chimney piece, stood a picture of her husband. It was the picture of a dead man: his smile had no confidence in it, his eyes were suspicious, his forehead was frozen in death. Wherever his widow moved about the room, the dead man followed her with his paper smile. That energetic jaw of his could not have abandoned life without a certain amount of difficulty. He was the child's father, framed in his role of useless observer, and he thrust up from the tomb like the eye of a periscope which is determined to see what is going on above the surface.

To the affections and injuries of the world he had left he offered his cheek stuck on cardboard, and always exactly as warm as the room itself. He had died, without anything being the matter with him, in a railway accident, and he appeared to be complaining night and day that it was unjust, that he had not experienced his fill of life, that he used to be despotic and jealous in his day. Near the photograph stood a bouquet of artificial violets in a pretty funeral vase—apparently the bouquet was entrusted with such small requirements as the dead man still possessed. It had full rights, and busied itself night and day in the secret business of covering, pacifying, anesthetizing, the dead.

Hélène stood up, displaying fresh signs of anxiety. She walked up and down the room. She could be heard saying aloud:

"I shall never get to the end of these invitations. What's the matter with me? It isn't difficult to write six envelopes and six visiting cards. It isn't much in a lifetime."

Rose had come into the room. She lifted her hands, and threw herself at her mistress's knees.

"Speak, speak, can't you!"

"I held him tight by the hand. I promise you that's how it was, ma'am. It was just outside the Galeries. And then someone or something passed in the crowd. Antoine wanted to see. And we got pulled apart. At first I thought I'd find him again right away. I called out his name in the crowd. People turned to see; I was so ashamed at the sound of my voice that I stopped, and I thought I should find him easier all by myself."

For an instant of silence the words she had just spoken passed slowly in front of the two women once again, passed at the speed of a hearse.

"Rose, Rose, Rose," said Hélène. And three times her voice changed its note.

"I didn't lose him, ma'am. It was more like as if someone stole him. But I should have heard him cry out. Why didn't he call after me?"

Rose took control of herself. She had just thought of the marvelous toys which Antoine had been getting from some unknown person, and she said to herself:

"Those toys are bound to be part of the secret. Why didn't I remember them before? They know the whole story, from the beginning to the end."

The eyes of Rose and Hélène met and parted. Hélène had also thought of the toys. Rose was thinking that they had been given to Antoine by the Danish gentleman who must be Madame's lover, or anyway soon would be. No doubt he thought it would advance his cause to give presents to her son: anonymous presents out of delicacy, though in each case he was obviously the giver.

The nanny did not approve of the friendship between Madame and the Danish gentleman. He seemed to her, after only one year of widowhood, as a useless luxury might have seemed, when there are so many poor people, so many cripples in the street. She recalled the odd circumstances in which these presents had been received. They came from no particular shop, and carried only a few simple words in an assumed handwriting:

"For little Antoinne" (sic).

Hélène had made the lightest of allusions to these toys in front of her friend, and he had blushed. Because he knew something about the whole affair. Or else . . .

Hélène and Rose stood there, facing one another, visibly hiding their thoughts, their hands behind their backs and their eyes lowered, their bodies so unquiet, so bare beneath their clothes that they might have been exposed to all the chill of the universe.

"Leave me alone," Hélène said.

Christiansen was tall, pink, and melancholy. His letters were collected in one drawer of her desk—a drawer which shut badly, and of which she often forgot to put the key in her bag. In the end she had taken him as her lover, simply because, when he was dancing, he always leaned over his partner with the air of a plant in need of its prop.

Little she cared now for an adventure into which she had merely stumbled by accident, or for a Scandinavian whom she had almost married by accident. She tore up the letters and threw them into a wastepaper basket. The phrase *love letters* seemed so idiotic, so empty, as she did so, that she could not stop herself from smiling, but she pulled herself back and murmured the name of her son: Antoine, Antoine!

She knew him so little, and yet he was so extraordinarily like her (the idea struck her now, and, perhaps, if she had not loved him more it was for that very reason): he was so troubled at the spectacle of life: in his own life he seemed always to be expecting changes: and she thought therefore, "Ah! a little piece of myself has escaped on holiday into the open world. Time is slipping and I'm doing nothing. I have only rung up the police. I don't seem to understand what has happened. My child has disappeared! Do I have to shout it out loud so as to show myself that it is true?"

She felt that any other mother would be telephoning all over Paris, rousing, in every quarter, at the end of the telephone, the specters of hope. But she could not make up her mind to telephone. A leaden garment carried her down into the depths, and she stayed in communication with the surface only through the narrow filament of a nerve on edge.

Why, oh why had Rose just said that someone or *something* had separated her from Antoine? Why a *thing?* There was so much that was strange in his disappearance. He had not cried out, his nanny had not been able to find him again. Why had he not come home? He was too intelligent not to have thought of giving his name to a policeman and to have had himself brought home.

Under the shock of what had occurred she felt feverish, and almost faint. Suddenly she thought with terror of her dead husband. How many are there of the dead moving among the passers-by in the street, recognized by none and bowing to nobody? But what could a ghost do with a living being whom he loved, and a child of seven at that? The hypothesis was ridiculous. Hélène repeated the word in silence, ridiculous, ridiculous, as if she hoped thereby to make it more ridiculous still.

Meantime, Rose, in Antoine's room, was leaning over the

wonderful toys. She thought: it might be a good plan to send them to the police; they might find a clue. But why did Madame not speak to her about any such thing?

Hélène came in unexpectedly. Rose jumped up, as if she had been caught misbehaving.

Hélène was thinking of something totally different. And somehow she took the nanny's hands—a thing she had never done before.

"Do you believe in ghosts, Rose, my poor Rose?"

"You should have a tisane, ma'am, and go and lie down."

"Do you believe in ghosts, Rose?"

"Oh, yes, ma'am!"

"Is that why you said just now that someone or something had snatched Antoine away?"

"It may be, ma'am, that that was why."

Hélène thought to herself that often one only understands afterward the real, the deep, meaning of what one has said.

There was a long silence. Rose left the room and went into the pantry. Passing her mistress's empty room she saw the light on, and turned the switch.

A few seconds later, Antoine arrived at the door of his home and lifted his eyes in vain toward the dark window of his mother's room.

At eleven in the evening, a telephone message from the police announced that "an accident seemed unlikely. None had been reported since six o'clock."

All night, in a frantic nightmare, Rose saw Antoine wandering on the roofs of the city. He was exploring them with the greatest care, carrying a creaking lantern. Next he was being pursued by a gray animal whose shape was not quite clear to her. Even when she was almost close to it, she could not be sure where it began or where it ended, and whether she was looking at the muzzle or the tail. It had a stiff, prickly coat, that was all she knew. When a street had to be crossed, she wondered how Antoine would manage. And she called out, "Stay on the roofs! Please, please, Antoine, don't cross without me. I'll be right there."

But Antoine kept forging ahead. Each time he was just about to tumble onto the stones below, when he was only a yard from the ground, he sailed up into the air again and reached the house opposite. Was he flying? His movements were more like those of a swimmer thrusting out arms and legs, and dripping with the night air the child climbed onto the roof by means of a straightforward pull, as if he were in a little boat lifted on the waves.

The animal, with countless claws, caught him just at the moment when Rose cried, "Don't be such a slowpoke, Antoine; hurry up. I mean what I say!"

She woke in a panic and sat on her bed until the fumbling dawn little by little relit the light of day.

All this time Hélène could not sleep. Why had Antoine not come in? Perhaps he wasn't pleased with the way in which he had been treated. Just what contacts had his mother had with him? One kiss each morning in her room, and one kiss each night in his. Isn't that the way with a good many mothers who live near the Porte Dauphine or in the Plaine Monceau? Rose adored the boy; she could not have handed him over to anyone more reliable. Let him come back, then! And quick! Even while she was arguing with herself, putting the pros and cons, she went through the motions of going to sleep. But her heart was still gesturing in the torpor of her body.

A piercing pain jolted her out of her drowse. She felt she might die if she moved. The doctor had advised her to take the greatest of care.

"The greatest of care? . . . ."

The words wore an odd color in the middle of the night. Next day at eight, she was brought a typewritten note: "There need be no worry. Antoinne (*sic*) is with me. He is very happy, and has everything he needs. If he ever wants to go home to his mother I shall bring him back *myself.*"

The last word was underlined. There was no signature.

"He's alive! He's alive!" Hélène cried. "He may be back at any moment."

But her heart was beating so painfully that the news could not have reached it. How long it takes for a message to thread its way through the opacity of our flesh!

At sight of the note, all fear of her husband's ghost had vanished. She turned toward his portrait and found it "just what one would expect in a photograph of the dead".

Feeling faint, Hélène lay back fully dressed on her bed and spoke to Antoine, as if between them there were no walls, no faces, no wastelands of open sky; as if nothing divided them but a few inches of familiar, of family atmosphere. She began to ask him the questions she had heard Rose ask. In doing so, she even took the nanny's accent without knowing she did so.

"Did you do your teeth last night before going to bed? And your legs?"

She had decided that he should enjoy a constant and single-minded love; she would think of no one else. She would never go out without him in, she would feed him herself (although for years he had been able to use a knife and fork perfectly well). She would have liked to teach him to read then and there, from a distance. In the morning, when she was dressing, she reserved his share of the hot water, she soaped him and dried him with care, and then, suddenly, there she was in tears. Her open chemise had revealed a lonely breast. Immediately she was angry with herself. "He's alive! He's alive!" and off she set, with Rose beside her, in quest of her son.

Should she show the note to the police? Must she tell them about the mysterious toys? Poor soul, some decision or other *must* be taken. She decided to do nothing for fear the police might start in search of Antoine themselves, with their heavy dirty hands and their eyes accustomed to all the grossness of life. She would make her mind up the next day, in the hope that Antoine might come back all by himself, carrying a little stick in his hand to show that he had been off on a lark.

She could not look at one of his photographs because she was so full of remorse at having forgotten to take him to the photographer's for so long. There he was, a child of four, quite unlike Antoine at the present day, quite unlike the little person she wanted above everything since he was alive, somewhere in Paris, with that face, that forehead, those hands, those rather square little knees sticking out above the woolen socks. Oh! Once more the idea of death mixed itself up with her affection for a photograph. Put it away! She walked to the cupboard and shut it inside with distaste. How many things are prohibited! Every second a fresh interdict arises. Notices with: It is forbidden to. . . It is particularly requested not to. . . Please do not . . . do not ever, ever!

In whose hands was Antoine? Who was the stranger who had smoothed out the note with the flat of his hand and who at that very moment was leaning over the table the better to watch him eat his breakfast? Breakfast! Did they give him any breakfast?

Hélène was less and less willing to eat herself, as though he would go without to the extent that she satisfied her own hunger. And to give him sleep, she knew she must lie awake, awake, awake!

V

"All round me, in different rooms, the future is asleep in narrow beds," said Bigua, who had gone to bed early the day after his theft. "Children grow in their sleep. Do you know what that means? The London children are growing, and so is the Parc Monceau child and the child from Passy. Their bones are not long enough for daily use and they grow in sleep. The cells multiply. And if I take them like a father in my arms, they will keep on growing while I hold them. How disturbing they are, these signs of growing! In children, too, whom I stopped in the street so as to make them my own children. Ah, you looked as if you had forgotten the existence of Colonel Philemon Bigua, and forgotten that among all the casual people in the street there are some people of *importance* who may leap all of a sudden into your life. You were walking one way, my little friends, and quite right too; you were quite in order until, until the moment when. . . . This way, my friends! Here we are at the Square Laborde; look where you're going; take care when you shut the door of the lift. I'm not shifting dominoes about in a box, but taking a hand, like God, in your fate."

The Colonel got up at five o'clock, put a poncho over his pajamas, and boiled himself some water on a spirit lamp. As soon as he had drunk a few cups of maté, he walked over to a horsehide screen which hid his sewing machine and his guitar.

He set the machine in the middle of the room and began to sew a piece of blue stuff which was gradually turning into a suit for Antoine.

He had done the same for *his* other children. In his heart he regretted that the latest to arrive had come wearing a new suit, since this diminished the importance of the work over which he was taking such an infinity of trouble.

Nobody was more gifted than the Colonel, whether with needle or with sewing machine, only too happy if he pricked his finger to the bone in the service of his children. To lodge, to nourish, to clothe these little people snatched from the turmoil of the streets—nothing could exceed his sense of privilege.

The wilful sterility of so many French couples revolted him. How soiled a face, he thought as he sewed, is worn by this Paris without children. There are such masses and masses of grownups in the streets that one would never be surprised to look into the cradles of the avenue du Bois and to find them full of fifty-year-olds, with cunning and anxious eyes, and brows lined from force of habit. If you so much as notice a child in the street, there are a dozen people watching it to see if it is alive!

He was mortified to think that a man like himself had no children of his own.

"And yet we are quite young!"

"We must think of something else," said Desposoria in a tone of resignation.

In shame at her own barrenness, she never overstepped the bounds of a humble silence.

It never occurred to Bigua that she might look at any other man with pleasure.

"When she calls someone handsome, or says what fine eyes he has, there is no feeling in her voice. She only knows that if his eyes are made like that they *must* be fine; they can be nothing else."

For years the Colonel had been frightened by women. He had never dared make a proposal of marriage—or any other kind of proposal—to one. But in his timidity he had often imagined himself going to see the mother of a family and saying to her, on an easy note:

"You may think I am rather daring, madame, but I am anxious to have children, and that must be my excuse. I have been thinking about your daughter—not that that really counts of course. Let us be quite clear about the matter: I don't at all want to dishonor your daughter (indeed it would be monstrous to do so), and of course she is charming and well brought up and she may easily marry a perfectly nice man one of these days. I simple want to have a child, that's all."

He had been working on it for three hours, and Antoine's suit was getting on remarkably quickly.

So much the Colonel noticed when he heard the pleasant rustling of his children behind the door of his room. The nurse was marshaling them, and giving them as many last-moment instructions as if they were coming to wish him a happy new year.

"Oh, nonsense," Philemon said to himself, "never mind these memories. I must put my expression in order. My logic, my reason, my kindness, my sincerity, come when I call you! We have to put the latest and the most extraordinary of these children at his ease! Everything has to seem natural to him—more magnificently natural than if he were at home. And I have to be as normal as the typical father when he takes up in his very own arms the child who is most like him!"

VI

The Colonel felt that he had no right to turn Antoine, Fred, and Jack away from his door. At night, he slept only with his head turned toward their rooms, ready for any sacrifice. The children liked to rush in unexpectedly so as to surprise one of his movements, to see how he took money out of his pocketbook and laid it on a tradesman's bill, how he thought, or worked, or did nothing at all.

"Look, he's going to smoke a cigar," they were thinking. "He's getting up. No, it's going to be a cigarette."

They brought him ash trays, each of them requiring his own ash tray to be selected.

"You're hardly making any smoke today."

As if he had been caught, Bigua began to puff out abundant clouds of smoke.

Sometimes, while he was reading, the children, hidden in a corner, watched him in total silence.

"What is he going to do with us—this man who is six feet away and has been pretending to read the same page for the last half-hour?"

One day, Antoine spelled out the titles of one or two files which were lying on the table: "Waifs and Strays," "Problem Children," and also sociological studies, and books on medicine and war.

Why did Bigua never laugh? Even when the children asked him to, the most he could manage was to pull a despairing face or utter a low funereal rattle. Did he even know how to smile? There was no illumination on his lips, not even a pale glow; nothing but a look of astonishment, frank and handsome, in his eyes.

Bigua could spend hours smoking, or drinking maté, a silver pipe at his lips and motionless. He scarcely ever read a book, since tucked away in his memory there was always some question to be settled first. He, who had once been a man of action, had turned into an astonishing dream factory, like those men who have lived long at sea or on the pampas: the horizon or the bedroom wall was always some untidy piece of news for them. If it chanced to rain, one day when he was meditating on the reasons which had induced President San Juan to play him false, the Colonel's annoyance became an endless downpour and all his memories dripped in rain water about him. No one better than he knew how to mingle his passing moment with the state of the weather, the color of the sky, the street noises, and the noises inside the house.

Antoine did not know what to think of this man who, after he had taken his hand among all the people walking down the boulevard Haussmann, little by little had effaced in him his mother's features, and changed the shape of his nanny's face—all by means of tales of travels by sea and on the dreaming plains across the sea. He felt a friendly feeling for his kidnapper, on account of the kindness and of the strange consideration which the Colonel showed to him and to the other children. Just as he also liked the exotic things which surrounded them—each of which was a glance, a spur to fresh delights, a peep show into the atlas.

And he was always talking about a wonderful journey.

"When?"

"Very soon."

"Immediately, perhaps."

"We're going to coax our way along all the continents of the world."

Even when he was not by them, he drew them and held them by his charm and his witchcraft. And he frightened them a bit, at times, when there was a gruyère cheese for dinner and he ate it rind and all. He had a grudge, at such moments, it seemed, against anything which was hard and inedible.

Bigua spoke of the children to his wife, using phrases such as "Our eldest, our youngest." One day, from the next room, they heard him ask:

"Do you remember, Desposoria, what a dreadful time you had when the twins were born? And how the nurse never came and never came. There was I busy unpacking the basket with everything you needed in it, myself. How lucky that everything ended all right!"

Desposoria smiled, mildly disturbed by her husband's calm imposture.

"Yes, thank heavens, everything went much better when the others were born, and after ten days you were up and about again."

One day Bigua said to his wife:

"We are going to give a party to introduce Antoine to our friends."

"My dear Philemon, I am often really terrified by the careless way you contemplate some of the things you do. Of course *I* admire them, but the law does not. You come and go peaceably, you eat and drink among a crowd of stolen children. *Que cachaza! Que pachorra!* And now you talk of giving a party and showing off the children we have *adopted*. Would it not be better to leave Paris? The police must be after you. And supposing the children denounced you? Danger has come to roost among us."

"Yes, I know I eat and drink with danger beside me, and

at night it comes and breathes in my face to make sure I am still there. But it doesn't alarm me; it is only one child more in the house."

VII

The Colonel had received news from home. Discontent against the President of the Republic was growing. Politically minded friends were writing to tell Bigua that they might need his presence, but that he must await the result of the elections. That would mean waiting four months.

"I shall not go without taking a girl from Paris. Among all the girls of Paris I must first choose my daughter," he thought. "Let all the parents of Paris tremble if they have a girl of the right age!"

And he went for lonely walks, looking right and left, among the twenty *arrondissements,* one by one. At four o'clock he might find himself standing before the door of a large school, and watching.

"It shall be the fourth to come out."

But they came out in large groups, and it was hard to tell which was the fourth.

Sometimes he followed a parade of schoolgirls down the street, murmuring:

"It shall be that one: I can only see her back."

And he hurried to pass in front. It was a hideous little girl, or a stumpy little creature, or else someone who aroused no emotion in him whatever.

When he went to the music hall, and a family of trapezists was announced, Bigua thought:

"It may be my daughter just coming on stage."

One day, as he was going off on the hunt, he thought that he was being followed. For several minutes he had heard footsteps behind him. He stopped in front of a shop, and the footsteps stopped too, at a certain distance. He felt that an odd adventure was brewing, irremediably. The back of his neck, better informed than his face, became extremely nervous.

Without turning round he thought, "I am caught. Scotland Yard or Sûreté Générale, or something much more important still?"

"Monsieur," said a voice behind him—a voice which smelled of burgundy laid down in flesh and bone.

At first he did not budge. He knew that his whole life might be at the mercy of one word spoken by a stranger.

"Monsieur, Monsieur le Colonel . . ." said the voice, coming closer, on a note of entreaty.

The Colonel swung round and his eyes met those of a tall man, looking slightly drunk, but lankily built. His eyes were blue or green (he seemed too poor to venture on eyes of any definite color, his face was red and, as it were, rubbed rough by poverty. He wore an overcoat crumbled away by gaping buttonholes.

"Well?" said the Colonel, in a fairly friendly voice. "What do you want? Do you know who I am?"

"I'm sorry, sir, but it's urgent. I must have a few words here and now."

Poverty never left the Colonel unmoved.

"If the poor knew just how miserable they make me feel, they could get my last piastre."

The man came up to Bigua, and said in a voice turned suddenly confidential:

"My wife is somewhat light-minded, General. But as for me, I'm not one of those tramps whom one sees everywhere. My name is Herbin. I've a trade. I'm a chief comp."

"And what may that be?"

"A compositor. Sir, I want to rescue my daughter; help me, I beg of you! I haven't always been an alcoholic. Up to just the other day I was working regularly in a big printing plant on the Left Bank."

"But, my dear friend, what can I do?" said the Colonel, hailing a taxi which passed so close beside him that it seemed to want a place in the story.

"I know how kind you are," said the man coming as close as anyone dares who knows that his breath smells of wine. "Come and see my daughter, take her away, keep her. You have already adopted other children."

"How do you know?" asked Philemon, his eyes staring, his ears pricked, his nostrils distended.

"Your concierge, M. Albert, is my cousin. I've even heard that young Antoine, your last, has not been *quite* adopted."

"What *do* you mean? Not quite adopted!" exclaimed the Colonel, so loudly that the passers-by turned round. "I shall deny nothing I have done, and I'm afraid of no one, and that's that."

"Oh, sir!" Herbin began again, in a duller voice than ever. "I am not here to reproach you with anything. On the contrary, I want to give my daughter into your hands. The fact speaks for itself, I should have thought. Come to her rescue, Colonel, come to the rescue of my angelic child! Come with me, come straight away," he went on with drunken insistence. "You know how rich you are. You are absolutely your own master. Come to my house! My wife is out . . . God knows where!"

"But, my dear sir, I have already too many children in the house," said the Colonel, pretending to cast aside the offer made him, with all the art of a horse trader; for all men everywhere use more or less the same stratagems.

"Come and see my daughter, Colonel Bigua. I shall trust you; you can let me know later; you shan't be committed to anything in advance."

The taximan was watching the two of them, as if he were trying to guess the subject of their conversation by means of a few fragments of talk or by the play of their expression. Suddenly he stopped his engine. That caught the attention of Philemon Bigua, whose mind was already made up.

"Let us go and see your daughter."

"A good girl," said the printer, getting into the taxi behind him, "but if she stays at home a few days more, she's lost."

As Herbin pronounced these words a large fragment of the sole detached itself from his shoe, just as Bigua was looking at it. With an angry movement, he knocked it under the seat.

"I have entire confidence in this alcoholic," Bigua thought. "Heaven knows why."

"I knew, Colonel Bigua, I knew you would not refuse to come with me," the printer said, and he laid his gray swollen hand on his neighbor's knee. "It means everything to us . . . the choice of a second father, a savior, for my own daughter!"

The Colonel began to feel curiously happy.

He had the strangest impression that all this had already occurred to him, or at least that it had been entirely foreseen, fore-willed. He felt as if he were prompting the printer in all he said.

"I know what, whatever the girl is like, even if she is covered with spots and sores, I shall take her home—solemnly in this very same taxi which will be waiting for me. Nothing can stop me now. This old rogue must have issued from one of my ribs, already dressed and stinking of cheap wine, in order to follow me in the street and offer me his own daughter to keep."

Bigua turned towards Herbin:

"But why do you insist on my interfering in your private life straight away? Why do you say that in an hour's time it might be too late?"

"How can I say it, sir? How can I explain?" And the red face became redder still. "My wife sees that the child is growing up . . ."

"Allow me, my friend, to inform you that without even seeing your daughter I adopt her, and I appoint you major-domo to one of my estancias."

"Colonel . . . My dear Colonel . . ." And his eyes became more brilliant than ever (they seemed to emerge from the bottom of the sea).

The printer held out his two hands to Bigua, who took only one of them, but made up for it by the warmth of his grasp.

The taxi was driving along the boulevard Saint-Germain. The situation of the two of them inside it became unbearable. They had shown too much fine feeling. So great a generosity soon becomes an affliction: they were overwhelmed by the weight of their open dealings. They needed to get out, to walk, to refix on their faces the primeval mask of dissimulation, or at any rate some degree of dissimulation, without which human beings cannot for long look one another in the eye without blushing. (How easily the face of man, stripped bare, becomes indecent!)

The Colonel followed Herbin up a wide staircase covered by a handsome carpet. This astonished him: he had expected to find himself in some kind of hovel. The printer kept chattering away in a loud voice. *There* lay a danger. One would have to try and cure him of drink, or at the very least, to dress him respectably and make him eat, by fair means or foul, so as to fight down the effect of so much alcohol for so long a time. Though perhaps it was only the threadbare state of his clothes which made him so talkative. His secrets seemed to come pouring out through the buttonhole rents, the leaky shoes.

The printer rang.

"I don't live here," he explained. "How could I?"

The maid led them into a discreet sitting room, furnished with taste, and in no way betraying that it belong to a prostitute. The Colonel, willy-nilly rather disappointed, kept glancing about in search of some scandalous, or at least equivocal detail. Everything was grave and orderly; the room seemed to expect that the door would be flung wide open to respectability.

Bigua looked. A pale girl, quite young, sensitive, trembling, came in. Her eyes were like her father's, but transposed into a sphere of purity, gentleness, surprise.

"Marcelle," her father said. "This is Colonel Bigua. You know who he is. He is willing to adopt you."

The Colonel bowed as he might have bowed to the wife of a general.

"Get ready quickly, before your mother comes in."

"How pleased I am," thought the Colonel. "By everything, by the drunk father, the child, the mother, and by my own useful self! The mother might come in with a pistol in her hand. And here I should be! And this discreet little room. And all fifty yards from the Seine, from that splendid river, and on the boulevard Saint-Germain! What could possibly be finer?"

They went down to the street and the American showed the child into the taxi. He took the printer aside:

"Do just as I say. Don't argue."

"Yes, Colonel."

"Then follow me."

The Colonel gave an address to the driver in a low voice. The father tried to make Marcelle sit beside Bigua, but Bigua motioned her to the folding seat, and invited Herbin to take the back seat beside himself. His face showed absolute gravity; for the moment it seemed fixed in a single expression.

A fleeting smile, dipped in alcohol, crossed the lips of the printer.

The child looked out of the window, wondering what part she was going to play in the life of this extremely well-dressed stranger.

For a good quarter of an hour the taxi drove among the gray houses of the town. It had crossed the Champs-Elysées, the place and the pont de l'Alma, the boulevard de Grenelle. Suddenly, as it was going along at full speed, the Colonel tapped at the glass and signed to the driver to stop then and there.

He got down, and asked the printer to follow him.

"Say good-bye to your daughter. You won't see her again for several weeks at least."

"Let me at least give her a kiss," the printer said.

"Why of course!"

He kissed his daughter on the forehead, but she, flinging her arms round his neck, seized him with violence.

"I want to come with you," she whispered to him.

"Dear girl, be reasonable," Herbin begged, in a low tone.

"Don't leave me, I want to go with you," Marcelle repeated through her tears.

The printer kept smiling at his child.

"No, stay here, stay here, my ducky," he said, and he pinched her arm sharply.

Marcelle shrieked, and fell silent, her face motionless, her tears frozen.

The Colonel wondered why she had made such a noise.

"Ah well, good-bye, my dear," said her father, in a caressing voice. "Be good. You have a new father now, a father such as I should have liked to be."

But he was in a hurry, feeling behind him, upright, the vast impatience of the Colonel.

"May I ask where you're taking me?"

"Monsieur, I want to do quite as much by you as by your daughter; I want to make you fully worthy of her. We are going to a sanatorium for alcoholics. In a few weeks you will be a different person. I suggest that you begin by getting rid of any alcohol you may be carrying in your pockets. You can throw it into the gutter."

"But I haven't got any at all!"

And in a few moments, Herbin went on in the lowest of tones, "Do you really think it is indispensable to put me into a home?"

"I am convinced, my dear sir, that you must be cured once and for all," said the Colonel, gently pushing him toward the doors of the sanatorium.

VIII

When the Colonel returned to the taxi after handing Herbin over to the director of the sanatorium, the child had disappeared.

The driver was questioned with some heat, and replied that it was not his job to stand guardian over his clients and that he would let all the little girls in Paris escape from his taxi, one after the other, if it was their pleasure to do so.

Bigua was too anxious to show temper. He repressed a strong desire to box the driver's ears, and softened his own expression little by little. Sooner or later the officers of any army always know how to be the most moderate of men.

"Which way did she go?" he asked politely.

"Get in; we can try and catch up with her," said the driver, his temper restored.

Two hundred yards behind a taxi, Marcelle was looking into the window of a shop which sold wood, coke, coal, briquets, and fire lighters.

"Mademoiselle," said the Colonel, holding his hat in his hand and bowing very slightly, "are you tired of my company already? Where would you like to be dropped? Give your orders to the driver yourself."

Marcelle was greatly embarrassed. "I was only looking into the shop window while I waited for you," she said.

And she climbed into the taxi.

Bigua all but exclaimed, "But I might not have seen you; I might have gone looking for you in the other direction and perhaps lost you forever."

Still, he said nothing, not daring at that second to ask a direct question of destiny. The age, beauty, pallor, nationality, of the girl greatly impressed him. And the color of her yellow dress, washed almost to nothing, and the clumsy way her stockings were darned, and the worn heels of her shoes, and her air of carrying the world on her shoulders! "Am I really

worthy of it all?" he asked himself. Not to speak of her per-
sonality still half-fledged and tiny, questing after its true
dimensions and its own flavor in a taxi crossing the fifteenth
arrondissement at full speed.

"I shall never dare invent a dress for her, nor even take her
measurements. And what will Desposoria say?" he thought.
He had left as much space as possible between himself and
the child sitting beside him.

When they reached home, the Colonel felt his satisfaction
all the keener on discovering that his wife and the children
had just gone out. He was singularly moved to think of himself
alone in the house with this child: a child with a fragile com-
plexion and chapped lips.

"Would you sooner have a room on the street or on the
court?"

"Oh, I don't need much room," Marcelle said, in a tone in
which the Colonel thought he detected a trace of coquetry.

That was all. But the phrase was followed by a significant
silence during which Marcelle never lifted her candid gaze
from the Colonel. The chief moments of that important day
fluttered back and died in her large eyes.

Bigua worked his face into a limpid smile, a carefully
selected smile. It was the first smile of his life. But immediately
afterward he could not help noticing that Marcelle was beau-
tifully built and that her expression wore a gentleness which
did not belong to childhood.

Outside it was beginning to rain.

The Colonel reflected that his wife would be back before
long. At any moment the bell would ring, and a few seconds
later his room would be invaded by children and by an excellent, placid wife at whom he could level no reproach except
that of having been his wife for the last fifteen years.

"Aren't you surprised to find yourself here, in the house of
a South American colonel? Did you know where I was taking
you?"

"I knew you were kind and foreign."

"Why did you run away from the taxi just now?"

Marcelle did not answer.

She thought: I am afraid of men . . . They have loud voices, they are much stronger than I am. I have seen such a lot coming into my mother's house like great dogs with their heads down, looking for a bone. They shut themselves into her room. Sometimes it was raining outside, just as it is now, and I amused myself by looking at their overcoats still warm on the peg, with papers sticking out of the pockets. As soon as I heard a noise I ran into the kitchen and made myself useful to the maid.

"And your mother said nothing?" Bigua broke in by miracle, as if he had been able to follow the thought inside her forehead.

She gave a little jump. It was as if Bigua had heard her thinking.

"Anyway, *I* don't frighten you," the Colonel concluded, with all the simplicity of which he was capable in a moment so complex, so weighty.

He had been wondering if he ought to say as much, or whether it were not the devil who had gone out of his way to put the words on his lips.

Marcelle said nothing. She lowered her eyes, and as the light was behind her it was impossible to say whether she flushed or turned pale.

The silence which extended between these two strangers sought out its size, its implications, and became filled with alarm precisely as knowledge deepened.

Bigua took control of himself. He said, in the loud, clear voice of the head of the house:

"Go and amuse yourself, my dear. The maid will show you the other room. Jump on the chairs, do what you like; my wife will be home before long."

He was easily carried away by his feelings, and then he was afraid of expressing them too mildly, although too often what he said went far beyond what he felt.

Marcelle was no longer afraid. She looked at the furniture in the hall with extreme curiosity. As for the smiling pictures on the wall, why, they were pictures of gauchos who were dancing like people in a dream. If she came close enough, she could read the signature: Fegari, or rather, Figari.

She could not help thinking: What will my mother do when she comes in? And where has this Colonel hidden my father? What was that great gloomy building where we drove him? She had meant to ask the coal merchant before whose shop Philemon had caught her. It was partly for that reason that she had walked off as she had; partly also from fear; partly because she was both spirited and independent, and that she wanted to show she was no longer a child who could be reduced to silence by a sharp pinch.

A handsome Negress wearing a cotton kerchief crossed the hall, smiling, and ducking in a kind of little curtsy full of encouragement. But she could not make up her mind what she was being encouraged to do. Or whether there were other children in the house; and whether they were bigger than herself; and if there were boys as well. What would the Colonel's wife be like? She was glad to think that the wife would soon be there. A door stood half-open. She pushed it wide and entered. There was a huge room on the other side, with a vast fireplace. A great black kettle stood proudly on a wood fire. There were chairs in cowhide and in one corner—frightful to relate—there were skeletons; two heads of oxen, horns and all, looking perfectly at ease. Here and there, in hidden pots, tall blue thistles made up a whole landscape. On the wall hung two guitars, two fine guitars of a comfortable shape. There was a portrait of the Colonel on horseback, in command of hundreds of horned animals, and, to match it, another portrait of Bigua, in civilian clothes, but surrounded by a whole army of cavalrymen, terrible to look at. She was not sure whether to be afraid or not. Or whether even to be surprised, or to run away for good and all from these savages so full of politeness and good manners.

Marcelle opened another door. Ah! it gave on to the hall. She began to understand the layout of the house. She had never imagined that there could be such large houses, and so mysterious, in the middle of Paris and in a quarter which she knew well. In the shadow of the hall—where she thought herself alone —she suddenly saw someone moving. It was another Negro, and he too began to smile kindly. Everybody seemed determined to put her at her ease. Still, she wondered why he had been stationed near the door of the staircase, unless he had been given orders to prevent her escaping. She wondered, further, whether he would have begun to brandish a long knife, or whether he would have let her go with the same gentle smile.

Marcelle quietly shut the door of the vestibule upon him. His expression of amiable concern never changed. She looked out of a window into the street. She saw the friendly rain of Paris, the friendly mud, the familiar gray buildings, two church towers, a dairy, a restaurant, and the Paris taxis, the little vans, the private cars, the passers-by, the street vendors, the Paris umbrellas. If she made as much as a sign in the falling rain a policeman would run up, and then others, as well as shop people and all the majesty of the law. She had nothing to be afraid of. All France was there to take care of her; in case of need her safety was assured among these foreigners whose presence in the Square Laborde had been authorized by the French government itself. It was most kind of this Colonel to take care of her, to part her from her mother, and to have accompanied her father to a place which seemed to have bestowed upon him a certain conscious dignity.

All this time Bigua, alone in his room, was working again and again over the events of the day. He thought:

"Why did I get into such a muddle just now? Can I really be pleased with myself?"

Desposoria came in with Antoine, Jack, and Fred. She could not help showing some surprise at her husband's new acquisition.

"Really you might have warned me in advance."

It was the first time since their marriage that she had showed even the mildest disapproval of his actions.

"How could I tell?" said the Colonel. He told her every detail of his adventure, except that he made no reference to anything he might know about Marcelle's mother.

"I shall go and give her a bath," said Madame Bigua, thus holding out an olive branch.

And she told the nurse to soap "the little girl" well.

Before long the nurse was bent over Marcelle's pale, fragile little form in a bath which bore the Colonel's coat of arms. But collecting her glance again when it had wandered from toes to head, she said, with a trace of irritation:

"You are quite big enough to soap yourself."

She sat in a corner of the room, with her back half-turned.

Marcelle's arrival among the other children made Joseph rather jealous. He was extremely pale, and long-legged, and he had awakened her curiosity when she saw him come in, throw his books on a chair in the hall, and give a couple of sharp kicks to a football, to the peril of a chandelier and of the glass in the picture frames.

She did not know that there was a boy of that age in the Colonel's house. He was rough, and he seemed willing to ignore her presence altogether; consequently she decided not to like him.

Although the Colonel and his wife did not introduce Marcelle to the other children, it was from no reluctance to do so but simply from natural creole indolence. The nurse merely told them that they might amuse themselves as they liked, and she shut the six doors of the hall so as to make the first stages of friendship easier.

Marcelle scarcely spoke. She sat still in one corner. As there were no clothes for her in the house as yet, she had been wrapped in a cherry-colored kimono belonging to Desposoria; and this disturbed the Colonel more than ever. He had avoided discussing with his wife the delicate question of what the child was to wear, and as he crossed the passage he pretended not to notice her. But he could think of nothing else all the evening: two hours ago he had not even known Marcelle, and now there she sat dressed up in his wife's things! He had never expected to bear any sentimental feelings toward that particular kimono, and yet it was linked now, and closely linked, with the most extraordinary adventure of a lifetime!

He recrossed the passage, walked through the little lobby which led to his room, and said to himself in front of the looking glass, "Excellent!" with a distressing pout of satisfaction. He found Desposoria in his own room, and, without any special motive, kissed her. She looked at him with amazement: generally speaking, he admitted only one pretext for tenderness, and she wondered if he were suddenly going to lock all the doors in order to make love to her, at six o'clock in the evening, in a room which was surrounded by so many children whom they had failed to put into the world.

But Philemon only wanted a book on the rearing of children from his shelves. For some time past the question of weaning had greatly interested him, and although he did not propose to steal a small baby, he was much agitated by uncertainty as to whether a child should be taken from the breast at fifteen or eighteen months. Today he could not concentrate on three lines at a time. He was thinking:

In which room has Desposoria put Marcelle? Why shouldn't I ask her? I might look as though I were too much interested in the child. So long as it is not in Joseph's room! But that would be absurd! My wife would never dream of putting her into the room of a fifteen-year-old boy. Who knows, though? Women sometimes forget the essential. And Desposoria, cold as she is, is perfectly capable of throwing them together just because they are the two eldest or for some other idiotic reason. No, it is quite impossible for her to have put Marcelle into the room of our one boy who is almost a man—if he isn't a man already. It is always in the deepest silence that these changes from boyhood to manhood take place, and one generally knows of them long after they have happened.

All the same, nothing could be more natural than to ask: Desposoria, which room have you given Marcelle?

Duty obliges me to take an interest in the girl. But why does my wife not tell me what I want to know of her own free will. It would be just as natural.

He rose in silence, crossed the hall, and visited the bedrooms one after the other. Ah, there was her humble little bag. The room gave on to the courtyard. In the layout of the apartment it was, excepting only Joseph's, the room furthest from the Colonel's. And it was beside Joseph's room. Philemon decided to lock the communicating door. It had already been done: Desposoria, excellent woman, had thought of it before him! The Colonel, still not satisfied with this precaution, took the key and threw it down the lavatory before going back to his own room. But he was soon back with a little piece of cotton wool so as to block the keyhole. He regained his room, crossing the hall with the busy expression of someone who is making an effort to look as though he were thinking of nothing; and he settled down beside Desposoria again, with his book open at a chapter, "On the Danger of Premature Weaning."

He began to read out loud, separating the syllables so as to force the words into his intelligence, obstinately though it was closed to any reading matter at that moment. He repeated:

"On the Dan-ger of Pre-ma-ture Wean-ing."

But the thought in his mind was:

At last a proper excuse for being alive has walked into the house.

So that's what a family at table is like, thought Marcelle. They are bringing a soup tureen into this serious dining room and lifting the hot lid in sight of people who are happy to be together. These, then, were the glasses, the plates, the dishes, of prosperity. And that was exactly how one had to behave in such company, exactly how one must speak, be silent, lift a spoon to one's lips, and wipe them afterward.

Marcelle had been placed on the Colonel's right, in Antoine's usual place.

She was rather pale in her kimono. The children and the servants kept staring at her. The Colonel alone seemed to find the matter perfectly natural, as natural as if, since the beginning of the world, God had decided it in a passing moment of leisure.

After dinner, they moved into the big room which had so astonished and enchanted Marcelle. In the huge fireplace, Philemon Bigua had had a *fogon* installed so as to recall the life of the ranchos. Pine wood from the Ardennes made just such a fire as one had in the pampas. It was not a mere decoration: early in the morning the Colonel grilled himself his *churrasco* from the Boucherie Gambetta upon it, and all day long the *pava* hung there, in case somebody wanted a cup of maté. Antonito the soldier-servant took care of it—Antonito, whose grandfather had been a slave, and whose gaze, still captive, rested only timidly upon a white face. Gumersindo, the black chauffeur (and so clever with machinery), Felizota the cook, and Narcisa the maid crowded silently round the fire, as soon as their work was done, as well as an old *peon*, Teofilo, who always went with the children everywhere, even when the Colonel and his wife were taking them for a walk. They all took part in the conversation, as they might on an estancia, in slow, intermittent, uninflected voices, which would have revealed even to a blind man the immense plains of America. They carried no smell of kitchen or pantry with them. All were wonderfully clean and shared with the family the use of bathrooms and running water.

As it falls out in the South American countryside, Europeans and creoles were sitting that evening cheek by jowl round the fire. There is nothing like the *fogon* to acclimatize the foreigner and to bring harmony into a heterogeneous assembly.

The Colonel took his guitar, and turned his back slightly

toward the printer's daughter (since he thought only of her and played for her alone); he began to sing some *vidalitas* dark with confused longing.

From the strings of the guitar, from the somber and smiling faces, from the patriarchal atmosphere in which masters and servants found themselves at one, from silences heavy with recollection, rose gradually, as though from the sea bed as a ship nears, one far-away country after another. The musical names of Argentina, Brazil, Uruguay, came to their lips along with the names of stopping places and ports where empty hearts lie on the quayside beside the tall packing cases filled with merchandise.

As they went their several ways to bed, the Colonel went into his wife's room for an instant and asked, in a voice which, though it did not mean to be mysterious, was plunged deep in mystery:

"And what do you propose to do with the personal effects of the child?"

(Why did I say "personal"? he thought. It must be so as to bring them closer to that small delightful body.)

"They are scarcely even worth throwing away."

"No, no, my dear, you must keep them and pack them up into a parcel which she can keep in her wardrobe. Remember that those are the things most her own in the whole world. In none of the five continents could you find anything, never anything, which belongs more to her. . . . Even China . . . though there . . ."

He stopped. He did not even try to express a thought which hovered at the back of his mind.

Three weeks passed. Marcelle could not think about Colonel Bigua without an odd sensation. He lived so determinedly among his dreams, to the point of spending hours on end without apparently doing anything, that the mystery surrounding him held her singularly attentive, and often obliged her to sit in her room keeping her dreams in tune with his rather than write out the lessons given her by her governess.

Marcelle was educated at home, the Colonel, her father (consulted by telegram), and Desposoria having decided that the company of unsuitable friends might compromise the work of purification which was being exercised upon her person.

She wondered whether Bigua still thought of her. Certain uneasy attitudes of his made her suppose that he did; and she noticed that his look often wandered toward her hands, the buckle on her shoe, or the top of her hat. One thing she knew: that she had long wanted to kiss the heavy eyelids behind which were hidden the blackest eyes, and the most expressive, she had ever seen.

To Marcelle he represented all that had been lacking in her mother's house: luxury, kindness, and foreign lands. She kept staring at him, always in the midst of his solitude, like the Wild Man of the Woods, hidden by twelve leagues of greenery.

She admired the abruptness of his face, the dead-white skin and the jet-black hair; she found him far handsomer and far more virile than any of the men whom she had watched coming into her mother's room, out of breath with expectancy and showing their impatience by their looks.

It sometimes happened that while the boys were playing she slipped quietly into a little drawing room of which the door, usually open, gave into the Colonel's room.

She liked to stay there, in the shadow of the closed shutters—whatever time of day it might be—so as to hear Bigua rustle a page, or give a commanding cough, to hear the small knock of the maté kettle on a plate, or to smell the cigar smoke which edged into the little drawing room in search of heaven knew what. There was a grave circulation of noise, smoke, light, thought, from one room to the other. Two silences, two hearts, flowed into a single channel, and one of them, blindly, never knew that the other was there. And over all there lay the emanation of size and strength which flows from a man when he is spied on by a little girl—and far from her home at that.

Curled up in a green armchair, Marcelle lay still. She liked to think that this queer man, so kind to her father and to herself, had only to take a couple of paces to find himself in the drawing room and lay her presence bare. But one day it was the Colonel's wife who came in and found her pretending to be asleep in the dim light.

The next afternoon, Marcelle came back to the same spot to listen and to remember. In her arms she held a doll which Desposoria had given her.

Bigua was still alone in his bedroom.

All at once, after some clearing of the throat, he began to speak:

"If I have left my country it is only because of the jealousy of the President of the Republic, who did not care for me."

"Perhaps he is talking about me," thought Marcelle from the depths of her armchair.

Philemon Bigua was thinking out loud, and in Spanish, all that his modesty would have forbidden him to say in the ordinary commerce of life.

"I was the moral victor at the battle of Pieditras. Flowers were strewn in my path."

Then a second later:

"A woman; a real one; that is, a French one . . .

"Certainly; or rather, why not? Certainly! . . .

"I pay 30,000 francs for this apartment, and I haven't even got a horse, or a cow, or an ostrich, or a teru-tero, or a barbed-wire fence! But I have a *fogon*."

After each reflection the silence of Paris, so delicately sensitive, gradually and with difficulty knitted itself together again.

"But if I really want a Frenchwoman," said Bigua, and in French this time, "I shall have to go to the *bordel*." He spoke in a ferocious tone.

And he began to walk, with long strides, up and down his room.

Marcelle had already given way to panic and fled.

Knowing that her husband sometimes thought out loud,

Desposoria, expecting a revelation of some kind, took the place of Marcelle in the green armchair on the next day. She waited. But the Colonel gave her no information or, at least, she was resigned to his silence and sat congratulating herself on his power of keeping his thoughts in for a whole hour, when a phrase fell on her ears, whispered in an undertone. She could not understand it, but the tone of the voice itself was utterly miserable. And in the middle of his phrase, Desposoria had heard her own name, so naked, so poverty-stricken, among these incomprehensible syllables, that she let fall her needlework and burst into tears. Meantime, Marcelle, who was tiptoeing in to take up her vigil once more, stopped short in the darkness just behind Desposoria; then she tiptoed out again without having been noticed.

Because she had seen Desposoria in tears, she imagined that the Colonel must have revealed his love for herself.

IX

A few days afterward, Philemon was out on a walk in the Bois with Desposoria, Antoine, Jack, and Fred. The car followed.

But what on earth had happened? Twenty yards from there (and *there* meant that portion of the huge world occupied by the Colonel's shoes), twenty-five yards at the very most, Bigua had just watched an event in process of formation, and then fully formed, very quickly, in a few seconds' breathing space. A woman had fallen on her side as if struck down by an invisible wave. Another woman, looking like a nanny, had uttered a cry. All along the path, the trees trembled until they seemed no more than the ghosts of chestnut trees.

And there was Antoine, making signs to the Colonel and to anybody else with a heart in his body to come. He had just seen his mother and his nanny passing by and had run toward them.

Although he had never envisaged the possibility of such a meeting, Bigua was not surprised. Like an ordinary criminal he congratulated himself on the fact that there was no one about. There was a park keeper who seemed to have noticed something, and to be coming toward them, but he was over a hundred yards away. Bigua thought he would have time to arrange everything before he could catch up with them.

Antoine must have had a word with his nanny. She was no longer excited, and greeted the Colonel with a set face, but without hostility.

And already Bigua, who always carried smelling salts in his pocket in case one of the children was hurt, was leaning over Hélène and bringing back to life, from the dim regions into which they had strayed, her eyes, beautiful in their distress. For the second time in his life, he smiled. And in a way which his various emotions, each at odds with the next, made more than ambiguous.

"You will be all right," he said, amiably, screwing down the silver top of the smelling-salts bottle.

Rose was on her way to explain everything to the park keeper, but her mistress stopped her with a colorless gesture. The man moved away, his back mistrustful, and his step marking an extreme reluctance.

"I am entirely at your orders, Madame," said Bigua, who had already given Hélène his card.

She had scarcely recovered her faculties, and only vaguely understood what was going on, but she hugged Antoine to her. He kept looking at the Colonel with pride and gratitude, and never let go of his right hand. His pallor was such that he was pathetically like his mother.

Hélène did not feel strong enough to hate the man who had stolen her child from her.

There was a long silence.

"What am I going to tell her?" Bigua thought. "I have absolutely nothing to tell her. Among all the convolutions of my brain there is not one single answer to be found!"

Hélène suddenly spoke, and at great speed. Her words started out like tears.

"But why, why did you do it?"

Desposoria, weeping, leaned toward Antoine's mother and spoke into her ear. There was no knowing what she said, or how she excused her husband. The two faces, one against the other, spoke and heard with passion.

"You have only to speak the word, Madame," Bigua said. "I shall call the keeper and give myself up."

There was a long silence.

"Please," she said. "Don't bring the police into . . . into . . . all this. I must be alone before deciding."

She got up, looking round for a car.

Desposoria offered her her own.

"Most certainly not," Hélène exclaimed, with warmth.

"But yes, mamma," Antoine persisted.

Hélène looked at Rose, and in the end all three climbed into the car, which was driven by Gumersindo.

When she reached home, Hélène locked the door of her apartment and drew the bolt as well. She took Antoine in her arms and hugged him. She was on the point of saying, "Tell me everything, let me hear the whole story. Quick, Quick." But behind the dark integument of flesh and bone, her heart made its protest. Joy tortured it no less than grief; the heart mixed and confounded the two in the glumness of a single physical pain.

She went into her room, shut the door, and made Antoine sit beside her.

"I am not very well, but stay here, so. Play with . . . with my glove box. Do you remember how you wanted to try my gloves on the other day, and I stopped you?"

She lay on her bed. Antoine looked at the gloves. They smelled good, but he dared not touch them.

As Hélène had a bad headache, she asked him to put out the light. The room was lit only by a feeble glow trickling in from the hall.

"I hope you don't mind being left in the dark. I'm so tired."

And then, a minute later:

"There you are," she said. "Oh, it won't last long. In a few seconds I shall light the light, and we shall laugh when we find each other again. Still, I hadn't meant you to come home to a house like this. It ought to have been so gay. But you have at any rate quite a new mummy, although she is rather fragile." (Why did I say "although"? she wondered. If only words would leave me in peace, when I am so close to a state in which all words will vanish in a flash!) She began again, with the horrible impression of being unable to talk to children:

"It is so wonderful for me that you appeared just now when I hadn't even seen you. I was going to walk along the avenue Henri-Martin. I shall never be able to thank you enough."

She was amazed at the ceremonious note in her own voice.

"It is very selfish of me to keep you there in the dark. Go away and amuse yourself, but don't go far. Stay in the hall and play with your tricycle. It makes such a pretty noise when you go by."

He did not answer; and in terror she jumped up and turned on the light.

With his head on his arm and his lips to the carpet just where he had rolled over, Antoine was asleep among twenty pairs of gloves—black, white, gray—spread out all round him. Some were plain and some were stitched.

Desposoria sent to ask how Hélène was feeling the next morning, and to give her a basket of orchids.

A few days later Antoine asked his mother to let him go and play with the twins at the Colonel's house.

She shuddered, and hid her face in silence behind her hands.

After talking the matter over with Rose, she gave him permission to go, with an ease which disconcerted her. (The reports she had received on the Colonel and his wife were excellent.) But it was agreed that his nanny should not leave him for an instant. She would use the occasion to learn something of the atmosphere in which he had spent the last three weeks.

Rose came back so much impressed by her visit that that very evening she rang up the Prefecture of Police to say the child had been found.

"Where?" asked a heavy voice, with some severity, from the other end of the line. In a sudden fit of trembling, Rose rang off without knowing exactly why. And Hélène approved.

After a short interval the telephone rang once more.

"Where, Madame, where has the child been found? You cannot set the whole police machinery in motion and then refuse to give any information yourself."

"He was with some cousins in the country," said Rose categorically.

"Excellent," said the voice with an ironical inflection. "Excellent."

And the police rang off.

In the months which followed, Hélène devoted herself wholeheartedly to her son. She became paler and paler among her gathering memories. Although Antoine had been found she kept on searching hopelessly for him. Her heart, unaccustomed to calm and tranquility, seemed unable to beat except under the stress of anxiety.

When she rose to go from one room to the other, she did so with a kind of shyness invading every limb. Her heart was tired and ill, and in the hope that it might forget her, she tried to avoid any movement, any elevation of the voice. She thought: "The dead are jealous, and are never contented until they have drawn us into their orbit. One of them has seized my heart so truly that he will tear it from my body one of these days. Oh! I know that on this chimney-piece or on any other I shall soon be standing simply as the portrait of a dead woman."

She scarcely dared ask her child any questions about his stay with the Biguas. Illness kept her imprisoned in an opacity from which she could never escape. All that remained for her, far away, was a weakening light: and that, struggling at the summit of an immense taper.

One day (a year had passed since the disappearance of Antoine) she determined to invite Bigua and his wife, in return for all the visits made them by Antoine and Rose.

She sat in the drawing room, waiting for her visitors; but it was only when they appeared, framed in the doorway, that her heart understood, suddenly and simultaneously, both that they were due and that they were there.

Stunned by the shock, she drooped her head and fell dead.

She had expected death, but still more some miracle which might prolong her life. She had made no will.

On the day of the funeral, Antoine went in the early morning to the Colonel's house, where he was kept for luncheon, for dinner, "and for ever," as Bigua asserted. Bigua committed himself legally, with the consent of Hélène's family (who lived in the country), to take care of him until he came of age. The parents supposed that this rich foreigner must have been Hélène's lover, and might even be Antoine's father. Three hundred miles from Paris they gossiped about the matter for a long time, and decided to make no investigations for fear of finding something unfavorable to Bigua and so of having to undertake the education of a child whom they did not know and who was much less prosperous than themselves.

The Colonel's whole family, even the little ones—Jack and Fred—who had been stolen from London, went into mourning, "out of a sense of fitness," as Bigua said. And the printer, seeing his daughter in black, bought a crêpe ribbon for his hat.

Bigua was much saddened by this disaster and haunted by remorse. He wondered if he were responsible for Hélène's death. In vain he kept repeating, "One human life, what is that for a professional soldier?" He was sad, serious and sad. Since love reminded him only of the misfortunes which it brings in its train, he now looked at Marcelle with the most deliberate indifference.

And thus, little by little, uneasily, two years passed in the Square Laborde and in the world around it.

PART TWO

I

The printer had divorced. But he was always putting off the moment of leaving for one of the Colonel's estancias. Bigua used to run into him in the morning, at the end of each month, walking up and down the Square Laborde. The Colonel always held out his hand as soon as he caught sight of him, and considered himself obliged to offer a formal invitation to luncheon.

He was sincerely glad to receive an authentic father at his table, and to show him his daughter dressed in a Lanvin dress. The luncheon always gave him a certain amount of disquiet. Ever since he had seen Herbin lose the sole of his shoe in the taxi, Bigua imagined—in spite of the care with which he was now dressed—that he might drop a cuff, or his tie, or one of the three wrinkles in his forehead.

Herbin spoke with extreme correctness. He wore his grammar at his finger tips. One might have said that while he spoke he was precisely crossing his "t"s, inscribing his accents without ever forgetting one, dotting the "i"s, never omitting a cedilla, and setting in italics the emphatic words. In this foreign household he enjoyed a modest triumph and blushed slightly, to underline the occasion, whenever Desposoria made a mistake in French.

The children kept quiet and watched him eat. Marcelle sat between him and and the Colonel, and laid down her knife and fork from time to time to examine her father with friendly attention, on the sly. She was fond of this man—this thin, weak, scarlet little man—who called himself (and was) her father; she liked him for his misfortunes and for the happiness which he had found for her outside her own home.

Just when Herbin was preparing to leave, the Colonel always took him to one side, with some ceremony, and maneuvered him into a corner—everyone perceived that it was so as to slip into his overcoat pocket a well-lined envelope. Then he wrung his two hands with so little spontaneity, in a gesture so dreadfully mechanical, that the air itself of the hall was tainted by it.

Directly the printer was gone, the Colonel, whose nerves had been strained by his generous gesture to the point of needing utter calm, took refuge in his room and began to sew the first thing which came to hand. He worked his machine furiously, uselessly, even disastrously—for sometimes he spoiled forever a fine piece of stuff, blue or white.

Marcelle grew up in a calm and respectability. The discreet and sober luxury in which she lived, Desposoria's exemplary life, Bigua's constant reserve, all pointed toward a marriage which could be seen approaching from the farthest distance, as in the wide plains of the pampas.

Desposoria could be found on her knees in prayer at any time of the day and in any part of the house. This was not, however, so much from natural piety as because she was alarmed for her husband's health. She realized that to have Marcelle in the house could only make him odder still.

Nobody could tell what went on behind that high, anxious forehead, and upon that face which could be watched as it made its precise response to each movement of the heart, not least when Bigua, of deliberate intention, thought that he was betraying nothing of his own mind.

Nobody could tell what the Colonel was up to, when he wandered about the house wearing a bowler hat, although he had not the smallest intention of going out of doors.

Sometimes Desposoria tried gently to take off the hat, but Bigua sprang back as if someone had tried to take away a living slice from his brain.

And Desposoria went off to resume her prayers.

II

One day, while Marcelle was undressing in her room, after a visit with the whole family, including her father, to the Cirque Médrano, she clearly saw the handle of the locked door which gave on to the passage turn, and heard it make a tiny noise.

Who could it be? Madame Bigua, who always came into her room without knocking? Or Antoine? One of the Negresses? A servant? The Colonel himself? Or Joseph? Yes, Joseph. He slept in the next room, and he was now a tall boy of seventeen. We scarcely know him as yet: and Marcelle knew him no better—except that indefinably he frightened her.

She had always been on her guard against him; for he was a positive, wilful character with solid fists, and one had to shy away from his equivocal horseplay in the darkness of the passage. His loud voice, still half engulfed in childhood and full of vague reproach (one did not know against whom), held sway in this part of the house.

When he was working, he wanted everyone to take part in his labors, and one could hear him in his room, or as he walked up and down the passage, shouting curses and phrases of argot tacked on to lines from Homer, Virgil, Racine. If he opened a door, it was with a bang, and generally so as to slam it back against the wall. All his politeness toward the Colonel and Desposoria scarcely protected him from rebuke. When he took up a spoon or a fork at meals, one expected him, in one brief preliminary movement, to grab at everything on the dish. He ate noisily, sinking his shoulders, and grasping his knife and fork like weapons of war.

One summer's day, at the risk of his life, he had climbed through an open window into Marcelle's room, but he had done no more than burst out laughing at the sight of her wearing a single stocking and wrapped in a dressing gown which barely concealed her nakedness shrinking behind the silk.

When he met Antoine in Marcelle's room he packed the little boy off to work at once. And there was an explosion of jealousy.

"Nobody does any work in this house but me!"

He was always giving the twins a fright by hiding behind doors or in the passage cupboards: in one of these cupboards he had been discovered half-suffocated. Or else he organized a hunt through the whole house to find out whether Marcelle were tucked away telling Antoine one of the exciting stories she had just been reading.

"But where does he come from, this Joseph of yours? Hurry up and tell us!"

Bigua was walking through the quartier Mouffetard one day, in search of a child who needed rescuing. He was marching along, listening for an unexpected cry or a sob, ready to plunge into disgusting stairways, and he carried a heavy revolver in one pocket as well as a flashlight which cast a sharp, icy illumination. And then, just as he was going down the rue Censier, what should he hear but a small regular sobbing from an open window. He studied the matter carefully, and perceived that the sound came from a fourth floor room. After climbing so high with the utmost precaution he had found half-open the door of an apartment on a landing which might or might not— so great was his emotion—have been the fourth.

He heard a groan, and advanced into a room where a child was lying in bed in high fever. Bed, mattress, and blankets were all jumbled into one. Over the child's head and all about him hung a dozen or more rotten hams, suspended from the ceiling.

Bigua pretended to be a doctor from the local hospital and spoke to the child for a moment or two with the utmost tenderness. All of a sudden, he felt cold particles of an unknown substance dropping on his head: he replaced his bowler hat and saw that his coat was covered with worms which had fallen out of the hams. As he discovered others which were wriggling over the child's bed, he caught up child, blankets and all in a single movement. As he left the room with his heavy feverish bundle he bumped his head violently against a ham which hung lower than the others.

His car was waiting close by, in a dark corner.

The Colonel's doctor diagnosed typhoid. For three weeks, Desposoria and her husband nursed the child with the utmost devotion, knowing nothing either of him or of his family.

Joseph never spoke of his past, as though the weeks of fever had worn down or rubbed away all recollection of it. Sometimes, in the middle of a conversation, Bigua stopped listening and wondered, as he looked at him: Is he legitimate or not? Was his father a thief or a murderer? Or a syphilitic? Was he in his own home when I took him in my arms? Was he really the unhappy child I hoped to find, or simply someone set apart because of his contagious disease—someone *more or less loved* by his parents, since they were taking care of him at home instead of sending him away to the hospital?

Bigua had taken careful stock of the room from which he had stolen him; but he had no idea what lay behind it.

He did not even know whether Joseph had really forgotten his own past. Bigua believed so, but he could not be sure.

After a whole year of treatment and of private lessons, Joseph, who by then was fourteen, and pale but vigorous, had been able to enter the Lycée Condorcet. To make him forget the quartier Mouffetard and what, in old days, was called "a low extraction" the Colonel had decided to put him to classical studies.

Three years later Joseph remained still unassimilated in his new milieu like an aspirin which refuses to melt in a glass of water. The Colonel, who rarely looked him in the eye, could not have told exactly what was the color of his eyes or the shape of his nose. He thought that his lips were drawn in a straight line, whereas they curved up. When he took a furtive glance at his face, he tried quickly to rid himself of what he saw. Should their glances meet, the Colonel found himself staring at two mocking eyes which seemed to reproach him for having tried to turn a childish misfortune to account in order to boast himself a hero. Joseph had decided that he was no more than an amusement for Bigua, a plaything for an idle man, a pretext to do a kind thing without taking much trouble. There is nothing to be grateful for: that was the sentiment in the boy's look. Don't suggest such a thing, Monsieur Bigua, or I shall despise you so deeply that life under the same roof will become impossible for both of us.

He sometimes left revolutionary papers lying about in the hall or even on the Colonel's desk. His movements, his phrases, his glances, were charged with a vague atmosphere of blackmail. And one day, from a chance word which he dropped carelessly into the conversation, Bigua saw that Joseph was perfectly capable of denouncing him to the police.

Another day, Bigua surprised him during dinner in the act of turning an insistent look upon both Desposoria and Marcelle, as if it only depended upon himself to compare and to choose between them.

"I must certainly have misunderstood what he was thinking," the Colonel said to himself. "The boy would scarcely have the cheek to think of such a thing while I am in the room!"

He pretended not to notice Joseph's insinuations, nor his insolence, but when a silence fell in the room, Joseph suddenly began to drum on the table or to make an innocent little noise with his fork against a glass. At that, Bigua exploded—and Joseph sat quiet. But a few minutes later, it seemed to Bigua that his adopted son was jeering at him from behind his napkin.

On Sundays and Thursdays, Joseph stayed in bed and gloated over the tiny sounds made by his neighbor in the next room as she got dressed: light raps from comb, brushes, and pins against the glass on her dressing table. He tried to picture the successive stages of her toilette. He burned to know exactly which she had reached. One morning he could not stop himself asking her through the dividing door:

"Is your petticoat on?"

She did not answer.

And he waited for her in the passage, astonished to see her all at once completely dressed; the hooks, the snaps, all were neatly closed. The mystery was under lock and key. Face, hair, and hands alone had kept their nakedness, as if they were still behind the door. A kind of regret lingered at the point of her breasts from under the lace and the secret *crêpe de Chine* which covered them.

So as to show that he was not deceived by the dignity conferred upon her by a dress lavishly buttoned, Joseph seized her round the waist and tried to give her a kiss. But she ran away.

Marcelle had always treated him as a vulgar fellow with whom it was better not to have any close dealings. However he might admire her new dresses she always pretended not to notice his ties, the dashing cut of his collars, or the striped triangle of his breast-pocket handkerchief. The outer darkness to which she had consigned him was becoming unbearable.

"It will be all very well for her to play the great lady, but one day I shall have her rolling her eyes up in a rapture which will be all of my making."

But that time is long overdue, he thought, one day when Marcelle had changed her dress. Am I afraid of a girl—when only a simple door cuts her off at night from the biggest boy in my class. Am I afraid of that virtuous look which she puts on to protect herself whenever she remembers her mother? And suppose her room was changed. Suppose the old boy came and slept there instead.

The biggest boy in his class: that he was without question. When all the others were drawn up in the yard he overshot the others—who were three or four years younger—by a good head. And sometimes he handed round scraps of pornographic literature, the interest and the virtues of which none understood but himself.

There was the lightest of knocks on the door.

"Marcelle, Marcelle, let me in," said a voice, cracking under the stress of emotion and the expectation of pleasure.

She had turned on the light.

Joseph's voice! This time she recognized it.

"Open the door," repeated the voice urgently.

Marcelle thought very quickly:

How does one manage not to open a door to someone much bigger than oneself, running faster, jumping higher, swearing violently if he wants to . . .

"Open it."

. . . someone whom one would find the next day facing one again.

There was the bell, shining close to her hand.

She was already putting on her dressing gown, and slipping her feet into her shoes and preparing to open the door with her left hand while in her right she held the bell like a revolver. But she thought she heard:

"You'll have to face me tomorrow."

She was so upset that her senses failed her. It felt as though the line had been cut which linked her ears to her mind.

Careful to make no slightest sound, she opened the door. The corridor was empty.

She could hear Joseph undressing with violence in the next room, upsetting a chair, pushing his bed up against the wall, and at last beginning to do skipping exercises, as it seemed by the hour.

Marcelle followed the noise of his feet on the carpet; she listened to the whistling of the rope. At last, when she no longer saw the channel of light which divided their two rooms, she fell asleep.

The next evening, when she set about bolting her door, she noticed that the key was missing. She thought of telling Rose of her anxieties, but she doubted whether Rose would keep them to herself. People might think that she had been encouraging Joseph. She only had to push the heavy bedside table up against the door to make it impossible for anyone to get by. Desposoria's good example had nurtured in her the desire for virtue. But then she thought of her mother, and she wondered. Whatever she did, wherever she hid herself, she feared that her body would secretly preserve its freedom to do what it liked.

For some time she put off undressing, but at length she had made up her mind to it, with her eyes fixed on the lock, when there came a light tap. She was about to push the bed so as to reinforce the barrier made by the table when Joseph, breaking in with a rush, noisily knocked over the little table and all that was on it: the photograph of Desposoria and Philemon arm in arm, an alarm clock, and an inkstand which broke on the floor. In hideous silk pajamas, Joseph was smiling through his usual pallor and smelled of the talcum powder which he had used for the first time.

Marcelle was trembling. After the loud appeal for help of the table overthrown there seemed no point in making any further gesture. They waited a few seconds, motionless, expecting some sound or other in the apartment. But already Joseph was locking the door with the stolen key and putting out the light.

Rose heard the noise. Sitting up in bed, she listened a moment, then decided to explore the corridor leading toward Marcelle's room. She could see from outside that there was no light in there, however, so she went back to bed, not without reproaching herself for letting the matter lie. She had felt old, tired, irresolute, ever since the death of Hélène. And in an incoherent way she was surprised to find herself still alive, and living under the roof of Antoine's kidnapper.

But next morning, she wasted no time in going back into Marcelle's room, so as to pick up, at the point where she had left it the night before, the thread of her interrupted activities. She knocked at the door, wondering whether it would be grief, or fever, or joy which would open it.

"You can't come in," said Marcelle's voice.

"It is Rose."

The door opened just enough to let her in, and she found a

pile of linen drying in front of a wood fire. Marcelle had the reddened hands of a washerwoman.

On the light-colored carpet, and on the door, there were stains of ink.

But already, without her face betraying any preliminary emotion, Marcelle was sobbing her heart out in Rose's arms. And Rose was doing her best to console her while reluctantly, and out of the corner of one eye, she looked with profound disquiet at the underclothes upon which the fire threw a long and insistent reflection.

Rose had seen Bigua coming out of Marcelle's room in her absence now and again, and she supposed that he was therefore the guilty party.

Marcelle felt the consolation and the pardon of someone whom she admired, so she said nothing and waited for the evening with a sadness in which was mixed a hidden delight.

That morning, she went out as usual with Antoine, Jack, and Fred. Rose walked ahead with the twins. Marcelle held Antoine's hand. He was her most reliable friend; she was sorry he was not older and that she could not tell him anything of the anxieties which were working in her.

"Would you like to be ten years older?"

"If I was, I should marry you."

She had known what he was going to say, but that day she wanted to hear him say it. Sometimes, when one is deeply worried, nothing is so reassuring as the expected, as a sight of all that binds us, with conviction, to our previous experience of life.

III

Every day, Bigua took the opportunity of Marcelle's morning walk to spend a few moments in her room. His eyes fell upon the dressing table at which she had been sitting, upon the brushes and bottles; he hurried past the bed—at which he never dared look squarely—and crept round to the chest of drawers: not to unveil its secrets but in order to scrutinize by daylight the visage of the drawers which he opened one by one and to see, in a sense, whether they were feeling all right.

He locked himself in so as to rub up the furniture and the ornaments with a chamois leather from his pocket: all this with the utmost secrecy.

"Oh, ink on the carpet! And on the door! And no key since yesterday! Why did I say nothing about it? Why didn't I do anything? And the strange noise in the night! Why didn't I come and see what was getting broken in this end of the house?"

"Lunch is ready!" said Rose to the children in the passage, using a voice which tried to be that of every day, and succeeded fairly well.

Philemon had lingered in Marcelle's room; he hugged the wall of the passage like a criminal, his back bent, the right-hand pocket of his coat bulging with the chamois leather. It was like a tumor badly hidden and thoroughly uncomfortable. Nobody noticed him.

It was the moment, then, when faces were due to come from all corners of the house to stare at one another across the dining room table.

During the meal, the Colonel said nothing. His face was like a dry torrent. He spied on Joseph, who ate disgustingly, as usual, and with so little embarrassment that Bigua began to wonder whether any notice need really be taken either of the missing key or of the noise in the night.

He made up his mind to watch Marcelle. Immediately, a small nervous trembling of her cheek or her eye (in fact, it ran from cheek to eye, zig-zagging like a lightning flash) warned him that something serious had indeed occurred. He had never seen anything like it on her delicate skin. He was burning with desire to ask her in front of everyone if she felt ill, but he put the question from him as an indiscretion.

So as calmly to make up his mind, Bigua took a long time cutting up the meat for Antoine and Fred, while he thought.

"Can it be possible that this child has let the boy into her room of her own free will? I have so often seen her looking at me with such utter innocence. Surely the noise of falling furniture must have meant that she was putting up a desperate resistance? Or did it only fall from joy during the rumpus while they were amusing themselves? Perhaps she is simply like her mother. I mustn't worry! I mustn't! It isn't yet time to throw the truth to the dogs who bay for it. First cut up the meat. The children are waiting!"

Desposoria seemed to suspect nothing. Her face wore a perfectly natural air—the deliberately natural air which is assumed by the wives of the highly-strung. They try to make everyone round them believe that everything is for the best in the most sedative of worlds.

"All the same, I can't condemn the boy just because Marcelle has a tic in her face," Bigua thought.

But after luncheon, when he met Joseph in the corridor, he could not stop himself stamping harshly on his toe. Joseph pushed him away with violence. Worried by this jolt to his feelings, the Colonel wondered whether he had really hurt the boy on purpose. He spent a whole hour in the hall, walking from one room to another in a fortified silence, from the battlements of which he fired his glances of distress, neither willing nor able to say a word to anyone. Antoine came to say good-bye before going out for a walk. Much as he had loved Antoine, he thought of him, now that he stood before him, as if he were a wooden manikin with painted socks and legs. It was not the first time that he had noticed in himself the sudden flattening of affection, as though the heart had undergone an earthquake shock. Great blocks of love tottered to ruin all unbeknown to him. And a long time after, he was amazed to see that where great tenderness had once been built there was nothing left but death. Yes, now he even found his sewing machine absurd, in spite of the thousand small pleasures it had given him every time he worked the treadle. But why think of that? It was really ridiculous to jump from the child to the Singer.

Alone in his room, after having persuaded Desposoria, much against her will, to go out, he decided to go to a locksmith and to explain to him "the idea of a chain fixing fast the door of Marcelle's room." He had thought of little else for twenty-four hours past.

He demanded a heavy key and the solidest of chains, preferably a double one. Nothing seemed heavy enough for him.

When she came in, that evening, the girl must have her gaze caught by the chain. The mute warning of it! the reproach! the threat!

"I hope you understand," he said to the locksmith, "it is for a girl's bedroom. Those silly creatures lose their keys, and one must have something to keep this key in place. It must be a heavy chain, persuasive but graceful, all the same, mustn't it?"

The old locksmith could not help smiling into his thick mustache.

The Colonel had bitten his lip. How silly of him to have told the old fellow that he wanted the lock for a girl's bedroom! He might as well have added her name, and the fact, that she was a printer's daughter. . . .

He was much alarmed lest someone come into the room while he was there with the locksmith, handing him the hammer, the nails, and the screws so as to speed the work.

But nobody came. As soon as lock and key chain were in place, the Colonel thought:

"The whole house will be talking about it! Or, worse still, nobody will talk to *me* about it—not even Desposoria, although she makes a round of the children's rooms every day. The silence will be appalling. Perhaps they are already beginning to treat me like an invalid from whom certain things must be hidden—certain things picked carefully out of the multiplicity of life!

"Of course I might change her room. But I should have to talk to Desposoria about that, and it would mean admitting to everyone that I know what has happened. Don't the lock and key tell the whole story out loud by themselves? I expect they do, but I don't want to *speak* of it to anyone. Yes, *speak:* that is the one thing I cannot do. But does not the chain speak all by itself? Isn't it speaking one endless dreadful monologue all day long at my expense? It's perfectly likely. But with my own mouth I can say nothing."

Desposoria's room was some way off, and she had heard no noise; still, she understood that something important, something which might entail disagreeable consequences, had occurred on the Tuesday night. Bigua, Rose, Marcelle, and Joseph had each appeared odd in a different way. Rose was avoiding her. Marcelle and Bigua never spoke a word during luncheon. Joseph chattered away between courses regardless of the fact that nobody listened to what he said. None of the four looked as if they had had any sleep during the night. On whom, though, did the guilt lie? Desposoria dared not look in their eyes. She was busy during the meal with the twins and with Antoine.

During the day, the Colonel's attitude increased his wife's concern without giving her any information. Her pride prevented her asking questions of anybody. She preferred to wait.

And she spent hours in prayer below the agonized ivory of a Spanish crucifix.

Late in the afternoon, while he prowled about in a dressing gown, with his bowler hat on his head, Bigua found her still in fervent prayer. On a chest of drawers, he found four candles lit before a statue of the Virgin.

"Who is ill? Why have you lit the candles?" he asked, in a tone so tragic that he was moved by it himself, while Desposoria, having heard him coming, hurriedly blew out the candles. Her effort to lull it had been enough to awaken Philemon's suspicion.

"No one is ill, Philemon. You know that perfectly well. No one is ill, thank God. The doctor hasn't been in the house for a whole year."

But the Colonel had already left the room.

Before she went to bed that night Marcelle noticed a new key fixed to her door by a double chain. She recognized the handiwork of Philemon Bigua. The key carried his signature. No one else could have carried out such an idea, or have done it in such a way, and so silently. So he *knew*. She thought of how he kissed her forehead each evening with such shyness, how he hardly touched the tips of her fingers when she gave him her hand. She thought of his handsome face, so constantly disappointed, at all hours of the day. And she wondered why he had not turned Joseph out of the house, he so brave and so irreproachable!

She had quite made up her mind to keep her wicked neighbor at a distance that evening. Bigua's dramatic expression stood between them now. With pleasure therefore she locked the door before undressing. But Joseph did not attempt to come in and merely whispered, after knocking gently on the communicating door:

"Don't imagine that this Homeric installation of yours would keep me out if I wanted to come through. But I'm sleepy tonight."

Next day, after luncheon, when Bigua went toward Marcelle's room (he was too much upset to remember the chamois leather) he was greatly surprised to find Rose there. She tried to slip out. But the Colonel found his own right arm extended to catch her by the sleeve. And he had time to think: So I am going to speak! The moment must have arrived without my feeling it coming.

"Rose, didn't you hear an odd noise in the house two nights ago?"

(I have begun to speak; now no one can say where I shall stop.)

"No, monsieur, I did not hear anything."

"Never mind; but stay where you are, Rose. What do you think of that chain on the door there?"

"The key was lost," said Rose, at a loss (but she did not lose control); "it was perhaps a good plan to fix the new one on a chain."

"Obviously, Rose. Thank you. I don't need you any more. You can leave the room, my dear girl."

What is the good of asking only half the question? the Colonel thought. I shall never make any progress . . .

And he saw that his long legs were off again in search of Rose elsewhere in the house. He found her sewing in Antoine's room.

"Come now, Rose, you are hiding something from me. You must tell me everything. Remember that you are speaking to someone of consequence, to a victorious officer who might have been President of the Republic. I am not the kind of person who would ever admit a half-truth, a semi-lie—never the kind of soothing and tasteless syrup one administers to the weak. I am the head and the judge of a family which I myself have *chosen* (he stressed the word): a family which I wish to be morally and physically healthy. Had Mademoiselle Marcelle not confided something to you? Something about a love affair? Has she never complained to you about *someone's* actions? Or put it another way: what do you think of Monsieur Joseph?"

"Monsieur Joseph is seventeen; it is a difficult age to be."

"He is nearly eighteen, and he is perfectly capable of upsetting a piece of furniture in the middle of the night without bothering about the consequences."

"Do you think so, sir?"

"I am beginning to be sure of it."

"Then he's a ruffian," Rose burst out.

"You have spoken the exact truth, Rose. Now leave the room. I no longer need you."

It was a quarter to four. Bigua had looked at his own watch.

In half an hour Joseph would be home. The Colonel had made up his mind.

"What has to be packed in the suitcase of a young man whom one is turning out of the house? A sweater, a shirt, a pair of drawers, two pairs of socks. An image of the Virgin. How about his razor? Yes, of course. Slippers? No, quite unnecessary. No writing paper or stamps. Nothing but the strict necessities. How about money? That's the crucial point. What do I mean exactly by money?"

And he pinned a thousand franc note to a woolly cardigan.

The Colonel was waiting for Joseph in the hall. He walked up and down, carrying a little bag in his hand. As soon as the boy rang, Bigua opened the door slightly, handed out the bag and said:

"Be off with you; I am putting you out of the house!"

"You're jealous, old boy," said Joseph, who had never before addressed him with such familiarity.

The Colonel lifted his hand to strike him, but, gripping the bag, Joseph was off down the stairs, without hurrying and turning back with a wink.

The Colonel had been stupefied by the boy's retort. Only one had to look at him. Joseph wore his heart on his face; and it was obvious that he was still thinking only of Marcelle. Perhaps it was that very look which had thrown them into one another's arms.

"To hell with education!" Bigua cried aloud in his own room. "My sacrifice has only helped Joseph. Suppose I threw everything to the winds? My situation in my own eyes is becoming more and more absurd! If I was the father of this wretched girl I should at any rate have the right and the duty to be furious at what has happened. The fathers of my own age would come from the ends of the earth to form a ring round my anger and to share it. But suppose they learned at the last moment that far from being the child's father I am only a jealous guardian feasting on the least of her looks and movements as a tiny gratification of my own desires!"

All the next day, the Colonel waited to be arrested; he expected Joseph to have denounced him. He did not share his anxiety with his wife, but she had guessed it, and every time the bell rang she hid herself and her white face.

That evening, alone in her room, she could not keep back her tears.

What a life was hers! In her own house, a scandal had broken out in which she imagined that her husband must be involved, and now she lived in fear of the police as well. That was all she could expect after fifteen monotonous years of married life, during which she had never had occasion to reproach herself! She carried modesty, or precaution, so far, that even when she went to the hairdresser, the dentist, or the pedicure, she had herself accompanied by Fred or his brother; it was the same every time she had to be in a room with any man other than her husband. She forced herself to be busy night and day with a horde of children to whom she could not feel herself genuinely bound; she saw nobody, issued no invitations, since the death of Hélène (for such was Bigua's wish), and almost all day long she felt in the house the heavy presence of her husband. He in turn only really noticed her existence for five minutes a week as though he felt every so often a need to make sure that she was really there: it was a weekly checkup rather than a sign of tenderness or even of affection. The rest of the time he spent alone in his room or wandering round the house, looking into the state of the switches, bulbs, taps, bells, locks, drains, combs and toothbrushes, and, since the dreadful noise in the night, having every plate and dish with the least chip in it thrown into the rubbish bin.

At mealtimes Bigua now avoided Marcelle's eye. She sat opposite him and a little to the left.

"Out of bounds," he thought.

Desposoria offered her husband two dark eyes of flawless perfection. From time to time he glanced at her so as to gather

Immediately after his things had been moved he met Marcelle in the passage and said, in tones of anguish, as though he had just given her contrary instructions:

"Lock your door tonight, Marcelle. A girl of your age must always lock her door at night, mustn't she?"

"I do it when I remember," she said with a laugh which, by imperceptible shades, gradually became a smile aglow with pleasure.

"Well, then, remember!" said the Colonel, much upset, and in his severest voice. He waited a long time to see whether she was really going to lock the door. But Marcelle dawdled splendidly and apparently spent ten minutes over each garment as she took it off. She had been in her room a whole half-hour and still she hadn't put her shoes outside the door.

No, there she was, after all; and back again in the room, shutting the door a second later.

But there was no sound of a key turning in the lock.

He wondered what she could be up to. Quite alone inside. But in fact did she know how the lock worked? Perhaps he ought to explain it to her straight away. No, that was ridiculous. She wasn't stupid. And besides, she must be half undressed, and it would scarcely be the moment to show her how to shut the door.

All hope was lost. Perhaps she meant to leave her room to hunt for a book in the bookcase of the little drawing room, as she sometimes did. She would lock the door only when she returned.

But then, since his ears were visibly pricked for any ghost of a sound coming from the next room, he heard her click off the light. She must be falling asleep (or thinking of him in the dark) with the door unlocked. He could get into her room without her making the smallest resistance. She was certainly waiting for him. It was hard to grasp all that that meant!

Bigua began to undress glumly, like a man who is about to

be shot after his pardon has been refused: he knows exactly where the twelve bullets are going to hit him.

He put on a dressing gown and lay on the bed without having the energy to undress altogether. The room, which since Joseph's departure had become accustomed to solitude, felt the heavy presence of a man who had come from a far country to suffer in it.

Marcelle tossed about in her bed. Bigua heard her, and he contemplated tying his legs together with the lassos which were hanging on the wall. But he dismissed this idea as a humiliation. With his lips pressed to the pillow, he groaned feebly. Fancy having reached his age in order to be ashamed of himself, and of his own manliness!

He turned on the light. The darkness had become unbearable.

Meanwhile, Marcelle had sat on her bed. She was wearing a thin nightdress which still smelled of the wardrobe and already of love. Its whiteness, and that of the sheets, could not prevail against the deep darkness of the room, so that, in order to have the impression of seeing her surroundings better, she gave a self-conscious little cough from time to time.

The noise made by the Colonel led her to suppose that he was preparing to burst in like Satan himself. She could imagine him burning mysterious herbs or reading the future in coffee grains. He was probably drugged, she thought. She could picture him injecting himself with a liquid which set him alight, and throwing himself on her bed in despairing flames.

Bigua had lain down again. Although no sound reached him from the next room any more, he blocked his ears or dug his nails into his thighs with a small, miserable pain. Silence fell from the height of heaven like a heady cascade, dashing from one level of the earth to another without ever meeting the least resistance .

Bigua felt that the sense of responsibility was escaping from him, as though through a large wound.

He bit into his pillow until all of a sudden, in terror, he rushed barefoot into the passage, towards the *fogon* where Narciso was asleep. The Negro, on his pallet bed, was sleeping with his head on his bare arm. Philemon woke him up.

"Come into my room," he said. "I am not feeling at all well. I don't want to be alone. We'll carry your mattress between us."

The Negro noticed that in the thick growth of his ink-black hair Bigua had long white streaks.

For an hour past, his hair had been growing white with extraordinary speed. When he passed in front of a looking glass on the wall of his room, the Colonel had thought that his hair was shining, but he had not noticed that it was gradually becoming white.

Bumping along the passage, buckled into a hump, went Narciso's mattress, his gray and white mattress. The tufts of wool sewn up in their prison made every possible difficulty. Narciso had wanted to load the lot on to his own shoulders, but Bigua insisted on helping him, and each, like a brother, took hold of one end. It slipped through their hands, and gave them a pain in the fingers. The two of them felt a sense of danger at the root of their nails.

The Colonel, making signs to him, implored the Negro to make no noise. They had to edge past the radiator, which got in their way, and then right up against Marcelle's room. She heard the mattress rubbing its muzzle against her door.

"Is someone ill?" she asked, anxiously.

Narciso looked at the Colonel, who signed to him that he was not to open his mouth.

Silence fell once more, ill at ease, hovering above the unanswered question. Marcelle stood up, and saw through the keyhole the two men and the mattress. Then she snuggled deep into her bed, and dropped at last into a discouraged slumber. Never would she be able to understand the man!

The Colonel made Narciso sleep across the door of his room.

He helped him to get the bed ready, fussed about the number of blankets on it, and made him lay his poncho upon the whole improvised structure.

Next day, he said to Narciso as soon as he was awake:

"My orders for this evening are the same. Put your mattress across my door. I may need you."

Comforted by the resolution he had taken, the Colonel went to get dressed and perceived that his hair had gone white in the night.

He did not know how to appear before his family with so dazzling a confession in his aspect. It really did not seem necessary to make all those white hairs, to display the brilliance of a pain which ought to have lain hidden in the darkest corner of his heart.

He stayed in his room the entire morning, and then sat down to luncheon, equipped with, and, as it were, protected by, his bowler hat. No one bothered about him. They were all accustomed to see him wandering round the house like that. Then, all at once, annoyed by eating with something on his head, Bigua laid his hat on the carpet, without saying a word—it was a gesture of the most alarming simplicity—and never raised his eyes for the rest of the meal.

There was such magnificence, such suffering, in his face, that the children were frightened and dared say nothing.

Bigua found a kind of relief in his obvious martyrdom. But he still had to show his white hair in the other rooms of the house. He had to exhibit himself in the hall, the drawing room, even in his wife's room.

When Desposoria hid her immense surprise, and pretended to see nothing abnormal about him, Bigua leaned over her bed and kissed her through a flood of burning tears which might have come from him, from her, or from destiny.

V

Meantime, Marcelle had taken her mind off Bigua so as to spend the day with Antoine, who by now was eleven. Having done his lessons, he went to look for her in the small drawing room, and they played together until dinner time.

Antoine liked making himself look older by sticking a little curly beard on his face.

Marcelle adored the oddness of his appearance, the contrast of the childish eyes trying to catch up with the masculine adventures of the chin. On the surface lay a lie; beneath it, a thousand engaging contradictions. Tufts of hair creeping up the cheeks were determined to gain the upper hand in spite of the colors of childhood still worn by the skin. They wanted to make a conquest of the little boy, heart and soul. They had already set about it, and it was not easy to see what was going to stop them. Marcelle saw before her a face as incomprehensible as a phrase of which the different words had been shaken up in a hat. She watched the confusion of the lips under siege, invaded by the beard from every hand. But Antoine's eyes had never been more limpidly childish. The lids, when he lowered them, were marked by a candor as bright, as meditative, as subtle as the irises which they hid. She looked at his undecided nose, and wondered how long it would take before it chose its career.

When Antoine came into the room, Marcelle turned toward him. Bigua could scarcely be jealous of the little boy and he allowed him to penetrate into the inner circle of his own life, false beard and all. Brotherly love, filial love, paternal love, lover's love, there they all were, in that big South American drawing room, with doors open and shutters closed. And then it came about that one day Antoine, who had been playing all morning on a trapeze in the Bois, fell asleep in his beard on the armchair in the drawing room. Marcelle sat in it too, beside him. The white-haired Colonel saw that in his sleep the little boy was holding Marcelle's hand. He drew them apart in grave silence, so that Marcelle looked at him askance and murmured:

"Why did you do that?"

"Because I love you both," Bigua said. He was not quite sure what the thought was which he was trying to express. But after a minute he decided, "I was thinking of Joseph."

Mechanical as it was, this gesture surprised the Colonel himself. He had not believed himself to be jealous of Antoine.

Sitting in the drawing room opposite Marcelle, Bigua followed her delicate outline with his eyes.

"But there must be something wrong with her dress, there by the belt. No, there isn't. It is Joseph still there! But she is still a child, she isn't old enough. Was Joseph, for that matter? What a horrible, frightful thing! Send at once for all the doctors of Paris! Let them spend hours on the case! Is she not typical of all the innocents who are innocents no longer? Let everything be done which must be done. I promise to look away during the examination."

He jumped up, in great agitation, went to shut the door of his wife's room, and then fell silent: he fell actively silent, gulping down a host of words jostling each other to the surface. He left the room, after giving another glance in the direction of the anxious belt.

Marcelle saw him examining her, and it was in Antoine's arms that she wept.

"So; Marcelle is having a baby," said the Colonel from the safety of his own room. "And there was I, hardly daring so much as to look at her for fear of getting her with child from a distance! And now she goes from one room to another carrying a fresh life with her, and she walks in the Paris streets and stops to look in a shop window and walks on again!"

A child was going to be born in the house. Evidently happiness was not intended for Philemon Bigua.

Back again, the Colonel opened the door and looked at Marcelle with a pity, a terror, a fatherly affection which disputed for place with love. He planted himself down, very upright, very close to her, motionless, and silent as the great Pyramid. Marcelle jumped up and tried to escape him.

He took her in his arms and hugged her. His tall head rose clear above her own and bent over to the nape of her neck. She felt a strange doubt: that it might be in order to console her that he was holding her in his arms. Between them, the little boy seemed to be trembling. Perhaps he really was trembling. Then the Colonel gave her a long, fierce kiss, turning to infinite tenderness. Her mouth was wet and salt with tears. But he drew back. No, he had been unable to bestow his kiss until someone else had set that small movement working behind the belt.

Next day he thought:

"What a stupid child! But I like her to be stupid. Both here and far away. Now I can look at her without fear."

There was a knock at the door. It was Narcisa, the Negress, who always came through the drawing room to reach her mistress's room, so as to avoid making a draught. She was hiding something in a silk scarf: a handful of grass from the Square Laborde, which was intended to replace the herbs of her native land: it would be tied round Desposoria's neck, and it was expected to make her better the sooner.

As Desposoria was no longer so ill, Philemon thought that he ought to tell her of the impending birth of Marcelle's child. In one glance, he had taken in her capacity for receiving bad news, and concluded that it was enough to bear the blow.

Just as he was beginning to speak, he imagined that his wife might suppose himself to be the father of the baby. He got into a fluster, therefore, and fell silent, as though to allow one more breath to the particular being who would cease to exist as soon as he had spoken. Desposoria looked at him with the special gentleness which can be put behind a look by a trusted lover. The Colonel understood that she was not in the least worried. And he began his sentence quite naturally and carried it through almost with triumph.

"You have taught me nothing I did not know. I saw what was happening a good fortnight ago."

And she added:

"I am to some extent guilty. I never ought to have left those two children in adjoining rooms."

"And me! And me!" the Colonel exclaimed. "How about me? Didn't I go and take her away from her mother—just so that this should happen here!"

"Hush."

"Yes, hush. Hush, till the end of time."

And a few seconds later, he began once more, with a terrifying expression of joy, which alarmed his wife:

"This is something we should all be delighted about, and yourself most of all, my angel, for I love you with my whole heart!"

Desposoria was embarrassed by the clarity of this confession and the fixed look on her husband's face, and she quickly turned to speak of something else.

Soon after, the Colonel said to Narciso:

"You need not sleep in my room tonight, I no longer need you. Do you realize that we are going to have a baby born in this house? I can't tell you any more than that, my faithful friend, but you must know that the child is to be accorded the utmost reverence."

A child is going to be born here, Philemon thought, back in his room again. This house, which I believed to be so totally barren, is going to bring a living thing into the world!

And Bigua forced himself to look upon the birth of the baby as repayment for years of waiting.

"Although I have neither son nor daughter, I have the impression that something like a grandson is being made ready for me, and that I shall only see this work when it is finished and brought to perfection."

The Colonel's incomprehensible humors began to get on Marcelle's nerves. He now seemed openly delighted by the state she was in. He kept saying:

"I need no longer go back to America. Happiness can be found in the Square Laborde."

VI

One day, as he was drinking his maté in the drawing room, sitting opposite Antoine and Marcelle, Marcelle began to laugh with such abandon that she could not even manage to hide her face in her hands.

"Go and swallow two mouthfuls of water without breathing," Bigua told her. He imagined that one could stop an outburst of this kind as if it were hiccoughs.

She laughed twice as much.

This gave Bigua the painful impression that there was something odd about his own appearance. At once, therefore, he began to think of what, at that very moment, could make him most supremely ridiculous in his own eyes, in Marcelle's, and in those of the Universe—which, whatever one may say, is always watching.

And it was that very thing which had occurred.

Looking down, Bigua saw that a small piece of skin was visible—discreetly but beyond all possible argument—between two of his fly-buttons.

He got up and fled, redder than red-hot metal. Not until he was behind the door did he arrange the matter. Almost immediately, he heard the slam of the big doors on the landing.

He fled once more, precipitately, as though someone were behind him.

He stopped a taxi. In the evening chill, he noticed that he was not wearing a hat.

"Driver, go to a hat shop."

In the taxi, he swore at himself.

On leaving the hat shop, the Colonel felt that his face was still as scarlet as ever: the narrow mirror in the taxi seemed to be there only so as to prove to him how permanent, how perennial perhaps, his shame was going to be.

"Cross Paris as quick as you can," he said to the chauffeur. "Stop only when I tell you to."

"I shall never go home. For *several generations to come* I shall remain grotesque. I have no children, you may say. No matter, do what you can about that. Rage has got the better of logic in me today. There is time for everything! I shall never see Marcelle again, nor Antoine, nor myself. While the taxi is driving on, a good half of me at least will be in peace."

He spoke out loud, waving his hands, and without the smallest restraint. When they reached Vincennes, he said to the chauffeur:

"To the Porte Maillot, and still faster!"

And then he drove to the Buttes-Chaumont, to Montrouge, to the Batignolles.

He thought it best to lean through the window and tell the chauffeur, while they were traveling:

"I am a foreigner, and I want to see Paris."

Though his first thought afterward was, How absurd that I can do nothing without having to justify my own actions to myself!

Dashing in all directions through the city in the hope of outstripping, of bypassing his thoughts, gave Bigua back some of his self-control at last.

After an hour of fugitive traveling through the fortifications, he telephoned home to say that he would not be home to dinner, that he was delayed by urgent business. By urgent business! "But my dress is perfectly orderly now; I could go anywhere, even to dine with the President! Never mind, I shan't go home! When one has verified a thing of this kind thirty times over and one is still uneasy, one is likely to remain uneasy for life, even naked in one's bath, with the door carefully locked!"

At last he decided to dine and spend the evening with Marcelle's father.

The concierge told him that the printer had just gone out, and would probably be found in a little restaurant which, as she explained, was on the corner of the rue Lepic and the rue des Abbesses.

"So long as he hasn't begun! If I can only catch him in time to take him off for a really good dinner."

The printer was eating his soup. His back was visible from the other end of the room.

"Perhaps it is too late to step in. A man who has already eaten his soup shows a manifest lack of intention to dine anywhere else that same night. Perhaps it would be better to invite him tomorrow. But can I wait till tomorrow? Can my thoughts be made to wait? Before tomorrow night they will have eaten me alive! Since I shall not dare present myself to Marcelle for the whole of tonight and perhaps for the whole of my remaining years, I might at any rate be allowed to invite her father to dinner: he knows nothing of my deplorable adventure. Adventure, indeed! What a word for that calamity! Although I shall call it whatever I like. I take the first word that offers!"

The waitress was already asking Bigua if he was going to eat something.

"No, nothing. I have to speak to that gentleman," he said, in the lowest of tones; and then, taking every precaution, he crept up to the printer, and touched him on the shoulder, but so lightly that his touch passed unperceived.

He stayed thus for several seconds, his outstretched finger almost on Herbin's shoulder. He was still wondering what to do next when he saw the waitress's eye on him, and said out loud:

"Good evening."

The printer jumped.

"Oh, please don't move," said Bigua, pressing him back into his chair. "I was coming to ask you to dine with us. But I see it is too late; you have already begun your soup."

"Yes, I've eaten my soup, I've eaten my soup," the printer said, in a voice which gradually filled with doubt, as though the fact were more than questionable. As if the soup itself, or what remained of it in the plate, must also doubt its own existence, and believe itself hors d'œuvre, or a cutlet or compote of fruit. Or even nothing: a soup in limbo.

"I have only just begun to eat, and I am absolutely at your orders. I come here every day and the owners of the place won't mind in the least if I finish my dinner somewhere else."

"But how about yourself?"

"Oh my dear Colonel, what can it matter to me? What are six spoonfuls of soup which had slid through my esophagus and into my stomach? They are really nothing, nothing at all," said the printer, with a laugh. "I have made no pact with any future course. I am a free man—thanks to you," he added, with the suspicion of a cringe in his voice.

A few moments later, they were in a luxurious restaurant.

Just as dinner was beginning, the printer, who was trying visibly to say something especially amiable, exclaimed:

"You cannot imagine what a relief it is for me to know that my daughter is in your home and in safe hands. She is all I have in the world."

"There is no such thing in the world as a safe place. Even underground the tombs are ravished."

The Colonel felt no longer the least pity for Herbin. He was about to embark on an excellent dinner, and Bigua looked at him cruelly. His misfortunes, his discouragement, required a positive zone of suffering all round him.

"There before me," he thought, "sits the father of Marcelle—

whom I love more than anything in the world, and who escapes me further every day, since everything escapes me. I should see myself condemned to the solitude of hell even if I stole, one after the other, all the children in the world.

"There sits a printer whom I have cured of his alcoholism, and whom I am making this evening drink the most fabulous wines first, and then liqueurs after. That is what my printer looks like: he couldn't look any other way! Celluloid collar, brown tie, an infinitely printerish look in his eye, and the long lines in his forehead which are trying to be more expressive than they really are."

"Do you know why we are here, just the two of us? It is because life in France is becoming impossible. There comes a moment when no roof, no sky, is big enough. I am going back to America, and I wanted to tell you so."

As a matter of fact, the idea of the journey had formed in Bigua's mind as he spoke, just as a far-off shore gains definition to an advancing ship. And the Colonel felt, while the words dropped from his lips, that he was lying less and less, or, in other words, that what during the beginning of his speech had been a lie was turning into truth, pure and unalloyed.

In the silence which followed, he thought, "Marcelle imagines that she can laugh in peace at me for my stupid absence of mind. On the contrary, she will have to pack her bags! And Antoine too, and everyone, even the black and the white servants. Their color is not of the slightest consequence! Everyone shall dive into his trunks and his cupboards. There shall be no room for another thought! I have made up my mind. All the shirts in the house shall go traveling. And so shall the trousers, and my tail coat. And we shall follow our luggage in silence to some great French port!"

The printer thought it his duty to raise some polite objections. His daughter was not very strong. The climate of America might not be healthy enough for her.

"But the city of South America to which we are going is, with Cape Town and Wellington in New Zealand, the health-

iest in all the southern hemisphere. *Besides,* you can come too,"
he added. At the unexpected sound of the word "besides" he
realized that it was superfluous, and that he was only replying
to the unspoken thoughts of the printer and not to what he
said out loud.

"Oh as for me, all I want is to feel that I am not entirely
useless," said Herbin modestly.

"You can do whatever you like, naturally you can. It has
never occurred to me to press my own wishes upon you—or to
act against your own, if you like that better."

He was thinking: "How odd to try to take him with us also,
to thrust his nose into the whole sordid story, when it would
be so simple not to invite him. He need only learn *the news*
a long time after, chilled by three weeks of traveling. Why need
our journey get involved with this father of hers, this non-
poisonous mushroom? I suppose I attach no importance whatever to his daughter's downfall simply because it has happened
in thoroughly respectable surroundings. But as a matter of fact,
the man eating opposite me, the man whose foot I touch every
time I move my own an inch forward, knows absolutely nothing of the event which is tormenting me from my side of the
sole Mornay which I am in the act of putting on his plate."
So much Bigua thought with icy clarity. "Perhaps the moment
has come to tell him all about it. But there is a further question: It may be a disgraceful act on my part to arrive with such
damaged goods at my mother's house. What a present to make
my family at Las Delicias!"

However, the idea of the journey had already been launched;
it had a life of its own independent of Bigua. He proposed to
let things take their course, bowing to an established fact
while the printer went on talking and he himself did not
listen, although he looked deeply into his eyes.

The printer fell silent, so as to drink.

"You are an admirable person," Bigua said, "and it was very
proper of you to ask just now whether the climate of Las Delicias would agree with your daughter."

Bigua was forgetting that the question had already been settled, that it was one which demanded no further commentary.

But Herbin was off again, saying no matter what, while the Colonel meditated:

"There is no time to be lost in getting away. Thanks to the Paris dressmakers nothing will be noticed when we arrive. Once at Las Delicias I shall be able to see to everything. I shall send her away to an estancia at the right time."

"Yes, my dear sir," he said affectionately, taking the printer's hand across the table (he was quite enchanted by the idea of sending Marcelle to have her baby on an estancia). "We shall all set off together. You will come with us. You must. You will see what a wonderful country we have over there, what skies, what plains, what grandeur in the landscapes. I am ashamed of rubbing it in. It is in all the geography books. But today all the American blood in me has risen to the surface again."

He ordered some more Pommard. It was their third bottle.

"Sometimes in Paris, in the middle of a family talk such as we have just been having, don't be surprised if an unexpected look comes into my eyes. It will just have traveled seven thousand miles, at extraordinary speed, from the backwoods of South America."

Bigua thought: "It is that American who stole the children. There can be no doubt about that."

He went on:

"The American is taller and wider in the shoulders than my European self. He weighs fifteen pounds more, and lives in the open air; he is not afraid of alcohol, and he is utterly shameless. He is accustomed to wide spaces, and he looks on the passers-by in the square Laborde and in the Paris streets—with the exception of yourself, of course, my dear sir—as a herd of wandering oxen which he drives straight before him. Whereas my French self, who has been formed gradually on this side of the ocean, gets caught up in excuses, assurances, and protestations of all kinds."

He went on talking for a long time.

The printer kept laughing, falling silent, laughing again, asking himself what was the best attitude to adopt.

They had finished dinner. The bill had already been paid for some time, and Bigua did not get up. He had still said nothing to Herbin about the state in which Marcelle found herself.

"Your daughter is really delightful," he said all of a sudden after a pause. "Ah! By the way, did you know that I turned Joseph out of the house? You can't imagine how wretched his manners were!"

"Really?" said Herbin, without the least anxiety.

"I could tell you something about that."

And he was going to begin, when the printer began to look at him fixedly and, to keep himself in countenance, blew his nose. His handkerchief was of dazzling cleanness. And so white that Bigua's story stopped on his very lips.

The Colonel got up, and the two men went out of the restaurant without a word. They parted at the door, after exchanging a light for a last cigarette. As they were still holding their hats in their hands, their scarlet foreheads met, and the Colonel jumped back quickly as though he was afraid of revealing, by contact, what lay behind the bones of his cranium.

He wondered whether to go home. Directly, or after sampling the pleasures of the town. How wide and hungry the street seemed this evening!

"How about going in here," the Colonel thought, turning into a dark street and stopping before the half-open door of a house too brightly lit. "Here at any rate, I am sure to be in the right."

He got home at about two in the morning.

"These are the walls of my house, this is the ceiling of my house, and the floor of my house. One doesn't think enough about these things which protect one so humbly but so securely against the infinite which lies all around. There are children asleep here. And the child who is no more than an embryo is asleep too. Perhaps he has waked his mother up to ask her whether there is any news from the grown-up world."

He heard something which sounded like a woman's voice. Desposoria, from her room, had just called him for the third time. She had been waiting for him to come in, sick with anxiety?

"Where have you come from at this hour?"

"I went to buy a hat."

Then after a silence:

"I met the printer and we dined together. And what have you been up to?" he asked his wife, in the voice he might have used to an old friend whom he had not met for years.

"I have been in bed for the last three weeks," she said, calmly, but with a faint note of reproach.

"Ah, how disgraceful of me!"

He knelt at the foot of her bed. He left his right hand between her own. He had given it to her when he came into the room, and it still smelled of the place he had just left.

And while she stroked his white hair, he fell asleep on the rug, exhausted and reassured, too reassured. For several moments, while she believed him still awake, she stroked nothing but sleep.

After a few seconds, he woke again sufficiently to say, with great clarity but without lifting his head:

"As soon as you are well again, we shall go back to America."

And he fell asleep again, this time for good.

The next week, as Bigua returned from buying the tickets for Las Delicias, he found his wife on the landing waiting for him.

Her face was thin, but lovely still, and it was shadowed by

a piece of news. The Colonel could not make up his mind whether the news was good or bad.

"Marcelle was not well today, while she was packing," Desposoria said. "It was nothing really serious. All the same . . ."

"All the same?"

"There will be no child born in this house. It is God's will, and I did not await your return to give Him thanks with all my heart."

Bigua said nothing, and shut himself into his own room so as to discover what he really thought of this piece of news.

V I I

Overexcited by the sea air, the Colonel wished his children had shown more clearly their joy at being on a transatlantic liner.

"Are you pleased, are you really pleased?"

He was not sure whether to give these phrases an air of exclamation, or of interrogation, so indifferent were the children's faces.

"One is never as happy or as unhappy in one's surroundings as one could wish."

But all the same, what a good setting for the children was offered by the childish sea, so close-packed with pranks and inadvertencies! Only young eyes had a right to look at it, he thought. How painful it must be for all that foam to feel the gaze of grown men and real women turned upon its extreme fragility. And suppose the boat was full of nothing but children whom I had snatched away from the stupidity of their parents. From one end of the rigging to the other, a vast show of these small stolen people, bathed in a seaside happiness. Once there was a boat of that kind and I was its captain . . .

At that moment Marcelle passed on front of him without

noticing him. She was gazing at the horizon and she wore a white dress. Never had she looked younger, more finely built. "Entr'acte, entr'acte, please! Let there be a truce upon the ocean! All I want to be is a man of the high seas without any recollection whatever of love."

And he rose to watch the waves mold themselves and tear apart before his eyes.

For some time he did not think at all; his brain was satisfied by the movement of the sea. If he reflected at all, he felt it was simply through waves, foam, spray, and through the porpoises which leapt from the waves and disappeared again forever. He thought of all the travelers leaning like himself over the rail, of their host of confused desires—uncomfortable arrows shot night and day from the heart and falling, into the salty water without ever reaching the horizon.

He shook himself out of this reverie over the sea's surface, where his gaze slid on without ever meeting an obstacle, and went back to his cabin (his cell, he thought) to lie on his bunk.

He looked at the square glass over the basin. It seemed excessively square to him. The handle on the door stood out as a perfect, an absolute oval. The carafe appeared with impetuous suddenness. The bottle of dentifrice, the shaving brush, the toothbrush, seemed to leap forward, to jump out of their skins. They stood in three triumphant dimensions. The white paint of the cabin, under the throbbing of the screw and the brilliance of the sea, possessed an extraordinary and consequential whiteness, to which it could never have attained on land. Every object possessed the force and the power of self-assertion which can be felt in the *trompe-l'oeil* of certain lithographs. They told the sea: We exist. I am only a mass-produced carafe, exactly like a thousand others, but, in mid-ocean, above the Gulf of Romanche, I exist, I exist, I exist.

"And you?"

"I? I am a man going to America, going more and more to America every second."

He pulled out his pocketbook mechanically and opened it as he often did when he was at a loose end, or so as to deflect his line of thought. He looked at some bits of paper . . .

"Here are the railway tickets and the cabin voucher of the printer who never turned up at the gare d'Orsay. I wanted to do him the honors of the sea, and he could not make up his mind to leave Paris."

Bigua pictured himself arriving at his mother's house at Las Delicias, with his adopted children.

They would call him "my spiritual father," as they had been told to.

To be back! After three weeks, to be back with his mother, his real mother, and real brothers and sisters at the end of the journey! In Paris, he had only had the mother, the brothers and sisters of his imagination, each without breath or body and hidden behind the ocean. There was a colonial house waiting for him, keeping its ancient habits of life, and lying under a blue sky without flaw. He could not wait to hear the live chickens being carried three times a week to the kitchen—as he had heard them at Las Delicias ten years previously. They were being carried by the poultry merchant who squeezed them too tightly under his arms.

Bigua was delighted to be alone in his cabin for the time being. On deck one always has the impression of being spied upon from all sides. If you stop a moment to raise your eyes you see a woman with a child in her arms, thirty yards away, watching you with a reproachful air from the steerage between the bars of the dividing rails. Or there is a sailor wiping down the portholes of the saloon with a swab; as soon as he catches your eye he starts work again with an air of concentration.

A boat was passing through the round of the porthole, and Bigua climbed to the upper deck to look at it the better. He watched it for some time, and before putting his glasses back in their case, he turned them vaguely to a mast up which a sailor was climbing with amazing agility. Like a god climbing back to heaven. The sailor's head was caught alive in the depths of the lens. He turned round, and the Colonel noticed that he was like Joseph, but he did not allow his imagination to dwell on such an impertinence and looked back at the boat again as it moved away—a recollection sinking little by little into forgetfulness.

All this time, Marcelle was wandering down the white corridors of the first class. They were generously lit and never knew night from day. The cabin doors were shut and all alike, and she was thinking of the differences, the possibilities which were concealed behind each.

On leaving Lisbon, as it was beginning to get hot, and she was undressing behind her curtain with the door half-open and attached by a simple hook, she suddenly saw Joseph appear, like spindrift. It was he. It was indeed he, in a sailor's uniform. It was he, brusque and marvelous as ever. They said nothing, but clung to one another in a steely silence, superposed on all the noises of shipboard.

Then, as she realized what had happened, she thought, "Ah! good boy, my lost sheep, my heart's blood, my sailor, my prodigal!"

"I didn't write because I knew I should see you again."

"You smell of ropes and tar and fresh air."

He remembered the way he had forced his way into her room at the Square Laborde, knocking over the table. Often he had dreamed that it would be the first thing he would find at the bottom of the sea if one day he were drowned: that table and the noise it made falling over. But there is no noise at the bottom of the sea! Though what indeed, what does it matter, our idiotic reality!

He had changed. There was a serene kind of tenderness in his gaze.

They did not speak of Bigua nor of the children, but only, between two secrets, of the boat's tonnage, its draft, its speed, and its coal consumption. And of Joseph's work. He was a deck hand.

"I can't tell you how good the others have been to me. I

tried to sell my watch. They wouldn't let me, and insisted on lending me a hundred francs. I spoke to them about you. They deserved it."

Desposoria was told by Rose that Joseph was on board. She was glad, without knowing why. Then, after saying her prayers, she decided that it was a misfortune, and that at all costs her husband must not know.

"Does Mademoiselle Marcelle know?"

"Of course she does!"

"Oh dear, oh dear!"

The two women fell silent. They left it to the silence to act for the best on their behalf.

Next morning, Bigua watched, from his porthole, the sun rising over the sea. He slept very badly on board. In order to see the better, he was kneeling on his bunk.

It was four o'clock. With bare feet, and dressed in a blue singlet, Joseph was throwing buckets of water on the deck, three yards from him.

"That is Joseph earning his living," Bigua said to himself, as if in a dream.

Then, brusquely, and in full possession of his faculties, hiding his face behind the curtain, he thought:

"But it is he! it is he!"

And after an instant:

"What will become of me?"

The thought returned to him, but gently now:

"There is Joseph who has gotten himself a job on board a South Atlantic boat. Did he know we were going to be on board? No matter, that is his business. There he is, in the merchant marine. He eats in a mess and he sleeps in a hammock. And meantime, all round us, there is the ocean which will only stop at Rio de Janeiro."

In the shadow of her cabin, Marcelle was looking on too. Joseph had just left her, and he was close at hand, paler than ever, washing down the deck. She spied on him, examined, him for a long time without being seen herself.

The dawn was rising, the unsteady dawn of a moving ship, born casually on the back of a nameless wave.

Every morning, from his cabin, Bigua watched Joseph's thin face go by, and he saw his naked feet, his hands. He thought that that tall boy had lived under his roof for several years. Joseph continued throwing water on the deck. And the dawns followed one another over the surface of the globe.

"That face passing and repassing in front of my porthole, that forehead, that nose, those lips, those eyes, that pale skin will end by getting the better of me."

One evening, toward ten o'clock, after they had already crossed the Equator, the Colonel saw a shadow, a sailor's shadow, Joseph's shadow, penetrate into Marcelle's cabin.

"Ah, God! Everything will begin all over again."

Then:

"Suppose one of the ship's officers tries to find Joseph. They are right not to care. Other people are always right. I deserve the reproaches; I need them too. I shall be here to see that nobody disturbs them. Yes, so that nobody disturbs them! Let everyone enjoy themselves around me, let them enjoy themselves in this boat where everything is polished and clean and scrubbed."

Estancieros, sellers of leather and wool, walked up and down in the companionway on to which Marcelle's cabin gave. One of them stopped from time to time to underline the deep importance of a gesture, of a vocal inflection.

Bigua was thinking:

"Through the fan above the door, Marcelle and Joseph certainly hear these people as well as I do. Their conversation, brings the three of us oddly close together."

They were coarse voices, and loud, in spite of the wind and the presence of the sea, which devours all noise.

"I want to see cowhide at three piastres before I die," one

of them was saying. "And I shall! Just think; I have known it at sixty centimes. And I tell you I found it pathetic."

"Pathetic, that's the word."

Their eyes were starting from their heads. They were almost in tears. They went on walking up and down in front of Marcelle's cabin. And then at last Bigua saw them make off toward the smoking room.

Soon after, Marcelle appeared, quite close to the Colonel, and then vanished. Not realizing that she was under observation, she made no attempt to hold back the delicious flush which had set its mark upon her cheeks. Bigua perceived exactly what she was feeling, and the depth of her pleasure touched each agonized vertebra in his spine. It was as though until this very moment, and without confessing as much to himself, he had still been in hopes, still keeping Marcelle apart for future happiness.

With an air of distraction, Marcelle came back, and leaned over the rails, close to the Colonel but without having anything particular to say to his profile, built of particles of icy disappointment. And she went away again.

The Colonel double-locked himself into his cabin, and began to write.

Joseph was determined to show his girl to his friends, and they all arranged to meet the next evening at eleven in the baggage room, out of the way of the officers.

One reached the hold by a flight of iron steps which had to be descended backward. When Joseph and Marcelle came down, the sailors were already sitting round a big impromptu table. Marcelle gave her cheek to be kissed politely and without the least affectation. The idea occurred to her just as Joseph introduced them to one another: the chaps I work with . . . my wife. There was a warm-hearted cheer in the half-light—warm-hearted but hushed, like a cheer from the subconscious.

She was enchanted to see such young faces, such athletic bodies. Her eyes roved from one to the other with an easy smile. In the air, as well as great kindness, there was a gravity which arose from the prevailing atmosphere, from the hesitations of these men who, at that very moment perhaps, were being looked for on deck, from the risk they ran, and from the vigilant presence of the sea.

They ate a soup made of cheese and onions—a marvelous soup such as never is eaten on land.

In spite of the ease on their faces, each knew that at any second an officer might come down and that the lights would then be put out in order to make a general escape the easier.

Sometimes a packing case gave a crack in the dark. It was not very easy to breathe in this happy confinement. And yet there was a radiant quality of fresh air on every face.

Bigua had followed Marcelle from afar, and he knew that she was in the hold with Joseph and some of the sailors. At the moment that she reached the stairway he thought his eyes had met hers. But she had not seen him.

Hidden in the shadow on a narrow gangway, Bigua waited, he did not know what for, a few paces from the door. Having seen the dishes and bottles go by, hidden under towels, he had deduced that Marcelle and Joseph were celebrating their engagement.

Suddenly, he was obsessed by a vehement wish to get into the hold, to explain that they were at liberty to look on him as the sponsor of their marriage. He went to the door, knocked twice, tried vainly to open it, and shouted through the keyhole in a voice ever more trembling, "Marcelle! Marcelle! Marcelle!"

But the noise of the engines made his voice and his blows on the door inaudible.

Deeply hurt at getting no answer, the Colonel climbed to the darkest corner of the ship, on the top deck, behind a lifeboat; there, safe from every eye, he sat down on the hard planks.

Nothing was between him and the water—neither iron bar nor wish to live.

"Up; keep your body upright and dive into the sea!"

In spite of himself, Bigua could not lie still in the tropical water. His legs and arms began to swim in the heavy clothes which pulled him down while just at hand, like a vast mass of despair, the hull of the ship glided by.

And by his right arm there was something uncomfortable which impeded his motions. It was his fat pocketbook, stuffed with papers, in the inner pocket of his coat. What a fool! He was taking his will to the grave with him, written the previous night with clauses in favor of his children.

The ship was already out of reach. He threw the pocketbook after it and followed hopelessly at a distance which suddenly became much larger.

Now he was immensely far off . . .

Paris, Atlantic Ocean, Uruguay (1924-1926).